Drug Addiction (Substance Abuse)

Addiction is said to exist when the body becomes so accustomed to the presence of a foreign substance that it can no longer function properly if the substance is withdrawn. Not everyone who uses drugs, legal or illegal, becomes addicted to them. The three most commonly used drugs—alcohol, tobacco, and caffeine—are legal and freely available, but they do not pose an addiction problem for all those who take them. Not everyone who drinks becomes an alcoholic; some people smoke only on weekends or special occasions; many people who drink coffee don't crave it all the time. Much research is focusing on the question of why some people become addicted while others do not, and scientists and nutritionists are providing some answers to the complex question of chemical dependency.

The reasons for addiction, according to most research, lie in the brain. A group of chemicals called neurotransmitters carry the signals between neurons in the brain. One of these neurotransmitters, dopamine, plays a pivotal role in transmitting feelings of satisfaction, arousal, and reward, so that every time we experience these feelings, we have the desire to replicate them by doing whatever it was that caused them before. This may account for the repetition inherent in addictive behavior.

Alcohol, nicotine, marijuana, cocaine, and amphetamines are a few of the substances that increase dopamine levels in the brain, and the more they are used, the more deeply these substances are associated with pleasure and reward, and the more profound the dependency. It is also thought that people who become addicted to a substance come to take less pleasure in things they used to enjoy. Through positron-emission tomography (PET) brain scans of addicted people, research has shown that their brains show less response to other pleasurable pursuits, such as listening to their favorite music, than do the brain scans of people not involved in substance abuse.

The pleasure elicited by whatever substance the individual is addicted to is so strong that it is difficult to eradicate, and even after years of abstinence, there are triggers that may cause the person to relapse. Research has shown that long-term drug abuse results in significant changes in brain function that persist long after an individual stops using drugs.

Signs of drug addiction can include a decreased desire to work and/or socialize, extreme drowsiness, inattentiveness, frequent mood swings, restlessness, personality changes, and a loss of appetite. Persons addicted to drugs may want to be alone, and lose their tempers easily. Drug withdrawal symptoms may include headache, insomnia, sensitivity to light and noise, diarrhea, hot and cold flashes, sweating, deep depression, irritability, irrational thinking, and disorientation. Not surprisingly, individuals who are addicted to d[...] ing the excru[...] ing a continu[...] drug at all costs leads [...] mal life, including broken personal relationships, [...] employment, and even criminal behavior.

People who become chemically dependent do so at different rates, and research is showing that susceptibility to addiction may be, in part, hereditary. Complicating the phenomenon of addiction is the problem of drug tolerance. With prolonged drug use, the body often ends up needing more and more of the substance to produce the desired effect and to prevent withdrawal symptoms. Some users end up increasing the dosage to the point that they die, or come close to dying, from overdose. In addition, addiction almost always has a powerful psychological as well as a physical component.

The nutrient program outlined below is designed to help those recovering from drug addiction. Unless otherwise specified, the dosages recommended here are for adults. For a child under the age of seventeen, use one-half to three-quarters of the recommended amount.

NUTRIENTS

SUPPLEMENT	SUGGESTED DOSAGE	COMMENTS
Very Important		
Essential fatty acids complex	As directed on label.	Good for reversing the effects of malnourishment common in those with substance abuse problems.
Liquid Kyolic with B₁ and B₁₂ from Wakunaga	As directed on label.	Fights stress and protects the liver.
Neuro Logic from Wakunaga	As directed on label.	Nourishes the central nervous system. Detoxifies the system. Encourages normal brain function.
Vitamin B complex injections	2 cc daily or as prescribed by physician.	Needed when under stress to rebuild the liver. Injections (under a doctor's supervision) are most effective. If injections are not available, use a sublingual form.
plus extra vitamin B₁₂ or vitamin B complex	1 cc daily or as prescribed by physician. 100 mg of each major B vitamin daily (amounts of individual vitamins in a complex will vary).	Can give the same energy boost as a cup of coffee.
plus extra pantothenic acid (vitamin B₅) and	500 mg 3 times daily.	Essential for the adrenal glands and for reducing stress.
vitamin B₃ (niacinamide)	500 mg 3 times daily.	Important for brain function. *Caution:* Do not substitute niacin for niacinamide. Niacin should not be taken in such high doses.
Important		
Calcium and	1,500 mg at bedtime.	Nourishes the central nervous system and helps control tremors by calming the body. Use chelate forms.
magnesium	1,000 mg at bedtime.	

Free-form amino acid complex plus extra L-glutamine	As directed on label, on an empty stomach.	To supply needed protein in a readily assimilable form.
	500 mg 3 times daily, on an empty stomach.	Passes the blood-brain barrier to promote healthy mental functioning. Increases levels of gamma-aminobutyric acid (GABA), which has a calming effect.
and L-tyrosine	500 mg twice daily, on an empty stomach. Take these supplements with water or juice, not milk. Take with 50 mg vitamin B6 and 100 mg vitamin C for better absorption.	Tyrosine and valerian root taken every 4 hours have given good results for cocaine withdrawal. (See AMINO ACIDS in Part One.) Caution: Do not take this supplement if you are taking an MAO inhibitor drug.
Gamma-amino-butyric acid (GABA)	As directed on label, on an empty stomach.	Acts as a relaxant and lessens cravings. (See AMINO ACIDS in Part One.)
Glutathione	As directed on label.	Aids in detoxifying drugs to reduce their harmful effects. Also reduces the desire for drugs or alcohol.
Lithium	As prescribed by physician.	A trace mineral that aids in relieving depression. Available by prescription only.
L-Phenylalanine	1,500 mg daily, taken upon arising.	Necessary as a brain fuel. Use for withdrawal symptoms. Caution: Do not take this supplement if you are pregnant or nursing, or suffer from panic attacks, diabetes, high blood pressure, or PKU.
S-Adenosylmethio-nine (SAMe)	As directed on label.	Aids in stress-relief, depression, eases pain, and produces antioxidant effects that can improve the health of the liver. Caution: Do not use if you have manic-depressive disorder or take prescription antidepressants.
Vitamin C with bioflavonoids	2,000 mg every 3 hours.	Detoxifies the system and lessens the craving for drugs. Use a buffered form such as sodium ascorbate. Intravenous administration (under a doctor's supervision) may be necessary.
Zinc	As directed on label.	Promotes a healthy immune system and protects the liver from damage.
5-Hydroxytryptophan (5-HTP)	As directed on label.	Aids with both stress and withdrawal symptoms.
Multivitamin and mineral complex	As directed on label.	All nutrients are needed in high amounts. Use a high-potency formula.

HERBS

❑ Burdock root and red clover aid in cleansing toxins from the bloodstream.

❑ Siberian ginseng helps those experiencing cocaine withdrawal.

Caution: Do not use this herb if you have hypoglycemia, high blood pressure, or a heart disorder.

❑ Milk thistle helps to detoxify the liver.

❑ Pueraria, a Chinese herb, has been used for centuries as a cure for alcoholism.

❑ St. John's wort is a good antidepressant and can help with withdrawal symptoms.

❑ Valerian root has a calming effect. Used with the amino acid tyrosine, it has been found to be helpful for those undergoing withdrawal from cocaine.

RECOMMENDATIONS

❑ Eat a well-balanced, nutrient-dense diet that emphasizes fresh, raw foods.

❑ Add high-protein drinks to the diet.

❑ Avoid heavily processed foods, all forms of sugar, and junk food. These foods are a quick source of energy, but are followed by a low feeling that may increase cravings for drugs.

❑ See FASTING in Part Three, and follow the instructions.

❑ Consider consulting a qualified acupuncturist. Acupuncture has been known to help addicts by decreasing stress, anxiety, and the craving for drugs.

CONSIDERATIONS

❑ There is no single treatment that will help all addicted people. Treatment needs to be tailored to fit the different needs and problems facing the individual.

❑ To minimize withdrawal symptoms, withdrawal from any drug should be done slowly. The dosage should be decreased gradually over a period of four weeks or longer. This task cannot be accomplished alone; most often hospitalization and/or professional help is required.

❑ Most people are aware that a drug overdose can kill, but many do not realize that these poisons kill in other ways as well. Angina, heart attack, coronary artery spasms, and life-threatening damage to the heart muscle may occur with the use of cocaine and heroin. All drugs weaken the immune system in one way or another. Chronic marijuana use can reduce the immune response by as much as 40 percent by damaging and destroying white blood cells. Without a strong immune system, the body is vulnerable to all kinds of infectious and degenerative diseases.

❑ Buprenorphine (Buprenex), a synthetic narcotic, taken either by itself or in combination with naloxone, a drug that prevents the "high" induced by narcotics, is sometimes prescribed for people who are dependent on opiates, and this treatment has shown some success. Methadone may also be prescribed as a substitute for illegal opiates.

❑ Many drug users suffer from malnutrition. Because drugs rob the body of necessary nutrients, those addicted to drugs need to take high doses of supplemental nutrients.

❑ Research has found that children of alcoholics are more

Substances That Rob the Body of Nutrients

Different substances deplete the body of different nutrients. Use the list below to determine which supplements you may need as a result of the use of prescription or over-the-counter drugs, including alcohol and caffeine.

Substance	Depleted Nutrients
Allopurinol (Zyloprim)	Iron.
Antacids	B-complex vitamins; calcium; phosphate; vitamins A and D.
Antibiotics, general (*See also* isoniazid, penicillin, sulfa drugs, and trimethoprim)	B-complex vitamins; vitamin K; "friendly" bacteria.
Antihistamines	Vitamin C.
Aspirin	B-complex vitamins; calcium; folic acid; iron; potassium, vitamins A and C.
Barbiturates	Vitamin C.
Beta-blockers (Corgard, Inderal, Lopressor, and others)	Choline; chromium; pantothenic acid (vitamin B_5).
Caffeine	Biotin; inositol; potassium; vitamin B_1 (thiamine); zinc.
Carbamazepine (Atretol, Tegretol)	Dilutes blood sodium.
Chlorthiazide (Aldoclor, Diuril, and others)	Magnesium; potassium.
Cimetidine (Tagamet)	Iron.
Clonidine (Catapres, Combipres)	B-complex vitamins; calcium.
Corticosteroids, general (*See also* prednisone)	Calcium; potassium; vitamins A, B_6, C, and D; zinc.
Digitalis preparations (Crystodigin, Digoxin, and others)	Vitamins B_1 (thiamine) and B_6 (pyridoxine); zinc.
Diuretics, general (*See also* chlorthiazide, spironolactone, thiazide diuretics, and triamterene)	Calcium; iodine; magnesium; potassium; vitamins B_2 (riboflavin) and C; zinc.
Estrogen preparations	Folic acid; vitamin B_6 (pyridoxine).
Ethanol (alcohol)	B-complex vitamins; magnesium; vitamins C, D, E, and K.
Fluoride	Vitamin C.
Glutethimide (Doriden)	Folic acid; vitamin B_6 (pyridoxine).
Guanethidine (Esimil, Ismelin)	Magnesium; potassium; vitamins B_2 (riboflavin) and B_6 (pyridoxine).
Hydralazine (Apresazide, Apresoline, and others)	Vitamin B_6 (pyridoxine).
Indomethacin (INH and others)	Vitamins B_3 (niacin) and B_6 (pyridoxine).
Laxatives (excluding herbs)	Potassium; vitamins A and K.
Lidocaine (Xylocaine)	Calcium; potassium.
Nitrate/nitrite coronary vasodilators	Niacin; pangamic acid; selenium; vitamins C and E.
Oral contraceptives	B-complex vitamins; vitamins C, D, and E.
Penicillin preparations	Vitamin B_3 (niacin); niacinamide; vitamin B_6 (pyridoxine).
Phenobarbital preparations	Folic acid; vitamin B_6 (pyridoxine); vitamin B_{12}; vitamins D and K.
Phenylbutazone (Cotylbutazone)	Folic acid; iodine.
Phenytoin (Dilantin)	Calcium; folic acid; vitamins B_{12}, C, D, and K.
Prednisone (Deltasone and others)	Potassium; vitamins B_6 (pyridoxine) and C; zinc.
Quinidine preparations	Choline; pantothenic acid (vitamin B_5); potassium; vitamin K.
Reserpine preparations	Phenylalanine; potassium; vitamins B_2 (riboflavin) and B_6 (pyridoxine).
Spironolactone (Aldactone and others)	Calcium; folic acid.
Sulfa drugs	Para-aminobenzoic acid (PABA); "friendly" bacteria.
Synthetic neurotransmitters	Magnesium; potassium; vitamins B_2 (riboflavin) and B_6 (pyridoxine).
Thiazide diuretics	Magnesium; potassium; vitamin B_2 (riboflavin); zinc.
Tobacco	Vitamins A, C, and E.
Triamterene (Dyrenium)	Calcium; folic acid.
Trimethoprim (Bactrim, Septra, and others)	Folic acid.

inclined than others to use drugs, including cocaine. These individuals are 400 times more likely to use drugs than those who do not have a family history of alcohol addiction.

❏ An individual can be addicted to substances other than illegal drugs. Many are addicted to nicotine, caffeine, colas, alcohol, sugar, and even certain foods. Although these addictions may not pose as great a health risk, withdrawal still may be painful and difficult. Those who use these substances may also be more susceptible to illness and disease because these addictive substances deplete the body of needed nutrients. (*See* Substances that Rob the Body of Nutrients on page 336.)

❏ A growing problem for substance abusers in these times, especially for those who use drugs intravenously and share needles, is the threat of AIDS (*see* AIDS in Part Two). Unfortunately, for long-term drug users, even this is not enough to deter them from continuing the habitual use of drugs.

❏ *See also* ALCOHOLISM and SMOKING DEPENDENCY in Part Two.

Dry Skin

A balance of oil and moisture is crucial for healthy, attractive skin. Oil is secreted by the sebaceous glands and lubricates the surface of the skin. Moisture is the water present inside the skin cells, and comes to the cells through the bloodstream. It is the water in the skin cells that keeps them plumped-up, healthy, and youthful-looking. Oil and moisture work together; there must be enough moisture in the skin cells, but there must also be enough oil to act as a shield, preventing excessive evaporation of moisture from the skin's top layers. Ichthyosis is one of several inherited skin conditions that cause the skin to lose moisture.

There are actually two types of dry skin: simple dry skin and complex dry skin. Simple dry skin results from a lack of natural oils. This condition most often affects women under the age of thirty-five. Complex dry skin lacks both oil and moisture, and is characterized by fine lines, brown spots, discolorations, enlarged pores, and sagging skin. It is usually associated with aging. The proteins that make up the skin—elastin, collagen, and keratin—may also be damaged by prolonged exposure to sunlight.

Dry skin tends to be dull-looking, even scaly and flaky, and readily develops wrinkles and fine lines. It usually feels "tight" and uncomfortable after washing unless some type of moisturizer or skin cream is applied. Chapping and cracking are signs of extremely dry, dehydrated skin.

Dry skin is most common on areas of the body that are exposed to the elements, such as the face and hands, but it can be a whole-body problem as well, especially in winter. It is probably primarily a genetic condition, but it may be caused (or aggravated) by a poor diet and by environmental factors such as exposure to sun, wind, cold, chemicals, or cosmetics, or excessive bathing with harsh soaps. Nutritional deficiencies, especially deficiencies of vitamin A and the B vitamins, can also contribute to dry skin. Fair-skinned people seem to be more likely than others to have dry skin, especially as they age; most people's skin tends to become thinner and drier as they get older. If all other causes for dry skin such as dermatitis, eczema, psoriasis, or seborrhea have been excluded, then it is most likely that the reason for dry skin lies in a combination of heredity, vitamin deficiencies, and poor nutrition. Many people have skin that is dry in some areas and oily in others. In the classic case of "combination skin," the skin on the forehead, nose, and chin tends to be oily, while the skin on the rest of the face is dry.

NUTRIENTS

SUPPLEMENT	SUGGESTED DOSAGE	COMMENTS
Very Important		
Liquid Kyolic with B₁ and B₁₂	As directed on label.	An anti-stress, anti-aging formula.
Primrose oil or Kyolic-EPA from Wakunaga	Up to 500 mg daily. As directed on label.	Contains linoleic acid, an essential fatty acid needed by the skin.
Vitamin A with mixed carotenoids or ACES + Zn from Carlson Labs	25,000 IU daily for 3 months, then reduce to 15,000 IU daily. If you are pregnant, do not exceed 10,000 IU daily. As directed on label.	Strengthens and protects the skin tissue. Contains antioxidants that protect the skin by neutralizing free radicals.
Vitamin B complex plus extra vitamin B₁₂	As directed on label. 1,000–2,000 mcg daily.	Anti-stress and anti-aging vitamins. Use a sublingual form.
Important		
Kelp	1,000–1,500 mg daily.	Supplies balanced minerals. Needed for good skin tone.
Vitamin E	Start with 400 IU daily and increase slowly to 800 IU daily.	Protects against free radicals. Used topically, it can minimize wrinkling. Use d-alpha-tocopherol form.
Zinc	50 mg daily. Do not exceed a total of 100 mg daily from all supplements.	Necessary for proper functioning of the oil-producing glands of the skin. Use zinc gluconate lozenges or OptiZinc for best absorption.
Helpful		
Ageless Beauty from Biotec Foods	As directed on label.	Protects the skin from free radical damage.
Collagen cream	Apply topically as directed on label.	Good for very dry skin. A nourishing cream that can restore a healthy tone to damaged skin.
Elastin	Apply topically as directed on label.	Helps prevent and smooth wrinkles.

Kelp	1,000–1,500 mg daily.	Supplies needed minerals, especially iodine, for better hair growth and healing of the scalp.
Selenium	200 mcg daily. If you are pregnant, do not exceed 40 mcg daily.	An important antioxidant to aid in controlling dry scalp.
Vitamin B complex	100 mg of each major B vitamin twice daily, with meals (amounts of individual vitamins in a complex will vary).	B vitamins are needed for healthy skin and hair. Use a high-stress formula. Sublingual forms are best for absorption.
plus extra vitamin B6 (pyridoxine) and	50 mg twice daily.	
vitamin B12	1,000–2,000 mcg daily.	
Vitamin E	400 IU and up.	For improved circulation. Use d-alpha-tocopherol form.
Zinc lozenges	1 15-mg lozenge 5 times daily for 1 week. Do not exceed a total of 100 mg daily from all supplements.	Protein metabolism depends on zinc. The skin is composed primarily of protein.

Important

Free-form amino acid complex (Amino Balance from Anabol Naturals)	As directed on label.	Needed for repair of all tissues and for proper hair growth. Use a formula containing both essential and nonessential amino acids.
L-Cystine	500 mg daily, on an empty stomach. Take with water or juice. Do not take with milk. Take with 50 mg vitamin B6 and 100 mg vitamin C for better absorption.	Needed for flexibility of the skin and for hair texture. (See AMINO ACIDS in Part One.)
Vitamin A plus mixed carotenoids	Up to 20,000 IU daily. If you are pregnant, do not exceed 10,000 IU daily. 15,000 IU daily.	Helps prevent dry skin. Aids in healing of tissue. Antioxidants and precursors of vitamin A.
Vitamin C with bioflavonoids	3,000–6,000 mg daily, in divided doses.	An important antioxidant to prevent tissue damage to the scalp and to aid in healing.

Helpful

Lecithin granules or capsules	1 tbsp 3 times daily, before meals. 1,200 mg 3 times daily, before meals.	Protects the scalp and strengthens cell membranes of the scalp and hair.

HERBS

❏ An infusion of chaparral or thyme may be used as a hair rinse.

❏ Those with dandruff can benefit from taking dandelion, goldenseal, and red clover.

Caution: Do not take goldenseal on a daily basis for more than one week at a time, and do not use it during pregnancy. If you have a history of cardiovascular disease, diabetes, or glaucoma, use it only under a doctor's supervision.

RECOMMENDATIONS

❏ Eat a diet consisting of 50 to 75 percent raw foods. Eat soured products such as yogurt.

❏ Avoid fried foods, dairy products, sugar, flour, chocolate, nuts, and seafood.

❏ *See* FASTING in Part Three, and follow the program once a month.

❏ Before washing your hair, add about 8 tablespoons of pure organic peanut oil to the juice of half a lemon and rub the mixture into your scalp. Leave it on for five to ten minutes, then shampoo.

❏ Try rinsing your hair with vinegar and water instead of plain water after shampooing. Use 1/4 cup vinegar to 1 quart of water.

❏ If antibiotics are prescribed, take extra B-complex vitamins. Also take an acidophilus supplement to replace the "friendly" bacteria that are destroyed by antibiotics.

❏ Do not pick or scratch the scalp. Make sure to wash your hair frequently, and use a non-oily shampoo. Use natural hair products that do not contain chemicals. Avoid using irritating soaps and greasy ointments and creams. Massage your scalp first before washing your hair.

❏ Do not use a shampoo containing selenium on a daily basis, even if it aids in controlling dandruff.

❏ If dandruff is persistent or symptoms seem to be getting worse, or if it appears in areas other than the scalp, consult your health care provider.

CONSIDERATIONS

❏ Some people have found that sun exposure helps clear up dandruff, but others find that it seems to make the problem worse.

❏ It is best not to use over-the-counter ointments for dandruff. They can often do more harm than good.

❏ Nizoral A-D is an antifungal dandruff shampoo.

❏ Dermatologists usually prescribe a cleansing lotion containing a drying agent with sulfur and resorcinol, or a medicated product called Diprosone from Schering-Plough, to clear up dandruff.

❏ *See also* SEBORRHEA in Part Two.

Deafness

See HEARING LOSS.

Depression

Depression affects an estimated 17 million Americans every year, making it one of the most common medical problems in the United States. It affects young and old, and is twice as common in women as in men.

Depression is a whole-body illness, one that affects the body, nervous system, moods, thoughts, and behavior. It affects the way you eat and sleep, the way you feel about yourself, and the way you react to and think about the people and things around you. Symptoms can last for weeks, months, or years. There are many types of depression, with variations in the number of symptoms, their severity, and persistence.

People with depression typically withdraw and hide from society. They lose interest in things around them and become incapable of experiencing pleasure. Symptoms of depression include chronic fatigue, sleep disturbances (either insomnia or excessive sleeping), changes in appetite, headaches, backaches, digestive disorders, restlessness, irritability, quickness to anger, loss of interest or pleasure in hobbies, and feelings of worthlessness and inadequacy. Many think of death and consider suicide. Things appear bleak and time seems to pass slowly. A person with depression may be chronically angry and irritable, sad and despairing, or display little or no emotion at all. Some try to "sleep off" depression, or do nothing but sit or lie around.

The two major classifications of depressive disorders are *unipolar* and *bipolar*. Unipolar disorders are characterized by depressive episodes that most often recur at least several times in the course of a person's life. Bipolar disorders usually begin as depression, but as they progress, they involve alternating episodes of depression and mania. As a result, bipolar depression is commonly known as *manic depression*. (*See* MANIC-DEPRESSIVE DISORDER in Part Two.) This section focuses primarily on various types of unipolar depression.

The causes of depression are not fully understood, but they are probably many and varied. Depression may be triggered by tension, stress, a traumatic life event, chemical imbalances in the brain, thyroid disorders, nutritional deficiencies, poor diet, the consumption of sugar, mononucleosis, lack of exercise, endometriosis, any serious physical disorder, or allergies. One of the most common causes of depression is food allergies. Hypoglycemia (low blood sugar) is another common cause of depression.

Heredity is a significant factor in this disorder. In up to 50 percent of people suffering from recurrent episodes of depression, one or both of the parents also experienced depression.

Whatever the factors that trigger it, depression begins with a disturbance in the part of the brain that governs moods. Most people can handle everyday stresses; their bodies readjust to these pressures. When stress is too great for a person and his or her adjustment mechanism is unresponsive, depression may be triggered.

Perhaps the most common type of depression is a chronic low-grade depression called *dysthymia*. This condition involves long-term and/or recurring depressive symptoms that are not necessarily disabling but keep a person from functioning normally and interfere with social interactions and enjoyment of life. Research has found that this type of depression often results from (unconscious) negative thinking habits. *Double depression* is a variation of dysthymia in which a person with chronic, low-grade depression periodically experiences major depressive episodes, then returns to his or her "normal," mildly depressed state.

Some people become more depressed in the winter months, when the days are shorter and darker. This type of disorder is known as *seasonal affective disorder (SAD)*. Women are more likely to suffer from SAD than men are. People who suffer this type of depression in the winter months lose their energy, suffer anxiety attacks, gain weight as a result of craving the wrong foods, sleep too much, and have a reduced sex drive. Many people get depressed around the December holidays; while most of them probably just have the "holiday blues," some of them may be suffering from seasonal affective disorder. Suicides seem to be highest during this time of year.

Foods greatly influence the brain's behavior. A poor diet, especially one with a lot of junk foods, is a common cause of depression. The levels of brain chemicals called neurotransmitters, which regulate our behavior, are controlled by what we eat, and neurotransmitters are closely linked to mood. The neurotransmitters most commonly associated with mood are dopamine, serotonin, and norepinephrine. When the brain produces serotonin, tension is eased. When it produces dopamine or norepinephrine, we tend to think and act more quickly and are generally more alert.

At the neurochemical and physiological level, neurotransmitters are extremely important. These substances carry impulses between nerve cells. Serotonin, for example, plays a role in mood, sleep, and appetite. Low levels of serotonin can lead to depression, anxiety, and sleep disorders. The substance that processes serotonin is the amino acid tryptophan. The consumption of tryptophan increases the amount of serotonin made by the brain. Thus, eating complex carbohydrates (not simple carbohydrates such as fructose, sucrose, and lactose), which raise the level of tryptophan in the brain (thereby increasing serotonin production), has a calming effect. High-protein foods, on the other hand, promote the production of dopamine and norepinephrine, which promote alertness.

The American Psychiatric Society estimates that 80 to 90 percent of cases of depression can be treated effectively, but that two-thirds of people who suffer from depression do not get the help they need. Many people do not seek treatment because they are ashamed, or they feel lethargic and despondent. In many cases, people with major depression only seek help when they are at the point of breakdown, or when they are hospitalized following a suicide attempt (an estimated 15 percent of chronic depression cases result in suicide). A good support system from friends and family members is often crucial in getting a depressed person to seek help for his or her illness.

The following nutrients are helpful for those suffering from depression. Unless otherwise specified, the dosages recommended here are for adults. For a child between the ages of twelve and seventeen, reduce the dose to three-quarters of the recommended amount. For a child between six and twelve, use one-half of the recommended dose, and for a child under the age of six, use one-quarter of the recommended amount.

NUTRIENTS

SUPPLEMENT	SUGGESTED DOSAGE	COMMENTS
Essential		
Essential fatty acids (Kyolic-EPA from Wakunaga, salmon oil, flaxseed oil, and primrose oil are good sources)	As directed on label. Take with meals.	Aid in the transmission of nerve impulses; needed for normal brain function.
5 Hydroxytryptophan (5-HTP)	As directed on label.	Increases the body's production of serotonin. It should not be used with other antidepressants.
L-Tyrosine	Up to 50 mg per pound of body weight daily. Take on an empty stomach with 50 mg vitamin B_6 and 100–500 mg vitamin C for better absorption. Best taken at bedtime.	Alleviates stress by boosting production of adrenaline. It also raises dopamine levels, which influence moods. (See AMINO ACIDS in Part One.) Caution: Do not take tyrosine if you are taking an MAO inhibitor drug.
S-adenosylmethionine (SAMe) (SAMe Rx-Mood from Nature's Plus)	As directed on label.	Works as an antidepressant. Caution: Do not use if you have manic-depressive disorder or take prescription antidepressants.
Sub-Adrene from American Biologics	As directed on label.	A dietary supplement for adrenal support.
Taurine Plus from American Biologics	As directed on label.	An important antioxidant and immune regulator, necessary for white blood cell activation and neurological function. Use the sublingual form.
Vitamin B complex injections	2 cc once weekly or as prescribed by physician.	B vitamins are necessary for the normal functioning of the brain and nervous system. If depression is severe, injections (under a doctor's supervision) are recommended. All injectables can be combined in a single shot.
plus extra vitamin B_6 (pyridoxine) and	$\frac{1}{2}$ cc once weekly or as prescribed by physician.	Needed for normal brain function. May help lift depression.
vitamin B_{12} or vitamin B complex	1 cc once weekly or as prescribed by physician. As directed on label.	Linked to the production of the neurotransmitter acetylcholine. If injections are not available, a sublingual form of B complex is recommended.
plus extra pantothenic acid (vitamin B_5) and	500 mg daily.	The most potent anti-stress vitamin.
vitamin B_6 (pyridoxine) plus	50 mg 3 times daily.	
vitamin B_3 (niacin)	50 mg 3 times daily. Do not exceed this amount.	Improves cerebral circulation. Caution: Do not take niacin if you have a liver disorder, gout, or high blood pressure.
plus vitamin B_{12} and	1,000–2,000 mcg daily.	
folic acid	400 mcg daily.	Found to be deficient in people with depression.
Zinc	50 mg daily. Do not exceed a total of 100 mg daily from all supplements.	Found to be deficient in people with depression. Use zinc gluconate lozenges or OptiZinc for best absorption.
Important		
Choline and inositol or lecithin	100 mg each twice daily. As directed on label.	Important in brain function and neurotransmission. Caution: Do not take these supplements if you suffer from manic (bipolar) depression.
Helpful		
Calcium and magnesium	1,500–2,000 mg daily. 1,000 mg daily.	Has a calming effect. Needed for the nervous system. Works with calcium. Use magnesium asporotate or magnesium chelate form.
Chromium	300 mcg daily.	Aids in mobilizing fats for energy.
Gamma-amino-butyric acid (GABA)	750 mg daily. Take with 200 mg niacinamide for best results.	Has a tranquilizing effect, much as diazepam (Valium) and other tranquilizers do. See AMINO ACIDS in Part One.
Lithium	As prescribed by physician.	A trace mineral used to treat bipolar (manic) depression. Available by prescription only.
Megavital Forte from Futurebiotics or multivitamin and mineral complex	As directed on label. As directed on label.	A balanced vitamin and mineral formula that increases energy and sense of well-being. To correct vitamin and mineral deficiencies, often associated with depression.
Nicotinamide adenine dinucleotide (NADH)	5–15 mg daily.	Enhances production of dopamine, serotonin, and noradrenaline, which are key neurotransmitters.
Vitamin C with bioflavonoids plus extra rutin	2,000–5,000 mg daily, in divided doses. 200–300 mg daily.	Needed for immune function. Aids in preventing depression. Buckwheat-derived bioflavonoid. Enhances vitamin C absorption.

HERBS

❑ Balm, also known as lemon balm, is good for the stomach and digestive organs during stressful situations.

❑ Ephedra (ma huang) may be helpful for lethargic depression.

Caution: Do not use this herb if you suffer from anxiety disorder, glaucoma, heart disease, high blood pressure, or insomnia, or if you are taking a monoamine oxidase (MAO) inhibitor drug.

❑ Ginger, ginkgo biloba, licorice root, oat straw, peppermint, and Siberian ginseng may be helpful.

Caution: Do not use licorice on a daily basis for more than seven days in a row. Avoid it completely if you have high blood pressure. Do not use Siberian ginseng if you have hypoglycemia, high blood pressure, or a heart disorder.

❑ Kava kava helps to induce calm and relieve depression.

Caution: This herb can cause drowsiness. If this occurs,

discontinue use or reduce the dosage. Do not use kava kava if you are pregnant or nursing, or if you are taking antidepressants. Long-term use of kava kava may result in dry, scaly skin and yellowish discoloration of the hair and nails.

❑ St. John's wort acts in the same way as monoamine oxidase (MAO) inhibitors do, but less harshly.

Caution: Do not use this herb if you take prescription antidepressants or any medication that interacts with monoamine oxidase (MAO) inhibitor drugs. Use it with caution during pregnancy.

RECOMMENDATIONS

❑ Eat a diet that includes plenty of raw fruits and vegetables, with soybeans and soy products, whole grains, seeds, nuts, brown rice, millet, and legumes. A diet too low in complex carbohydrates can cause serotonin depletion and depression.

❑ If you are nervous and wish to become more relaxed, consume more complex carbohydrates. For increased alertness, eat protein meals containing essential fatty acids. Salmon and white fish are good choices. If you need your spirits lifted, you will benefit from eating foods like turkey and salmon, which are high in tryptophan and protein.

❑ Omit wheat products from the diet. Wheat gluten has been linked to depressive disorders.

❑ Avoid diet sodas and other products containing the artificial sweetener aspartame (NutraSweet, Equal). This additive can block the formation of serotonin and cause headaches, insomnia, and depression in individuals who are already serotonin-deprived.

❑ Limit your intake of supplements that contain the amino acid phenylalanine. It contains the chemical phenol, which is highly allergenic. Most depressed people are allergic to certain substances. If you take a combination free-form amino acid supplement, look for a product that does not contain phenylalanine, such as that made by Ecological Formulas. Phenylalanine is one of the major components of aspartame.

❑ Avoid foods high in saturated fats; the consumption of meat or fried foods, such as hamburgers and French fries, leads to sluggishness, slow thinking, and fatigue. They interfere with blood flow by causing the arteries and small blood vessels to become blocked and the blood cells to become sticky and tend to clump together, resulting in poor circulation, especially to the brain.

❑ Avoid all forms of sugar, including normally "good" sweeteners such as honey, molasses, and fruit juice. The body reacts more quickly to the presence of sugar than it does to the presence of complex carbohydrates. The increase in energy supplied by the simple carbohydrates (sugars) is quickly followed by fatigue and depression. Stevia, a concentrated natural sweetener derived from a South American shrub, does not have the same effect on the body as sugar, and does not have the side effects of artificial sugar substitutes.

❑ Avoid alcohol, caffeine, and processed foods.

❑ Investigate the possibility that food allergies are causing or contributing to depression. *See* ALLERGIES in Part Two.

❑ Have a hair analysis to rule out heavy metal intoxication as the cause of depression. *See* HAIR ANALYSIS in Part Three.

❑ Keep your mind active, and get plenty of rest and regular exercise. Studies have shown that exercise—walking, swimming, or any activity that you enjoy—is most important for all types of depression. Avoid stressful situations.

❑ Learn to recognize, and then to "reroute," negative thinking patterns. Working with a qualified professional to change ingrained habits can be rewarding (cognitive-behavioral therapists specialize in this type of work). Keeping a daily log also can help you to recognize distorted thoughts and develop a more positive way of thinking.

❑ If you are suffering from situational depression—depression that occurs in response to an event such as in the death of a loved one or the breakup of a relationship—try using *Ignatia amara*. This is a homeopathic remedy derived from a plant, Saint Ignatius bean, that helps control emotions during periods of extreme grief and hysteria.

❑ If depression is seasonal, light therapy may help. Exposure to the sun and bright light seem to regulate the body's production of melatonin, a hormone produced by the pineal gland that is, in part, responsible for preventing the blues. Stay in brightly lit rooms on dark days. Keep all draperies, curtains, and blinds open and use full-spectrum fluorescent lights in your home. The normal room has about 500 to 800 lux of light. Choose one room and light it with about 10,000 lux of full-spectrum light and spend at least half an hour there each day. For information about devices for this type of light treatment, contact either The SunBox Company or Apollo Light Systems (*see* MANUFACTURER AND DISTRIBUTOR INFORMATION in the Appendix).

❑ *See* HYPOTHYROIDISM in Part Two and take the underarm test to detect an underactive thyroid. If your temperature is low, consult your physician. Thyroid dysfunction is behind many depressive disorders.

❑ Try using color to alleviate depression. *See* COLOR THERAPY in Part Three.

CONSIDERATIONS

❑ Depression is not a natural part of aging, but it is frequently linked to age-related nutritional problems, such as B-vitamin deficiencies or poor eating habits. Older people who suffer from depression are as likely to benefit from treatment as a person in any other age bracket.

❑ Tyrosine is needed for brain function. This amino acid is directly involved in the production of norepinephrine and dopamine, two vital neurotransmitters that are synthesized in the brain and the adrenal medulla. A lack of tyrosine can result in a deficiency of norepinephrine in certain sites in the brain, resulting in mood disorders such as depression. The effects of stress may be prevented or reversed if this essential amino acid is obtained in the diet or by means of supplements. Mustard greens, beans, and spinach are good sources of tyrosine.

Caution: If you are taking an MAO inhibitor drug for depression, *do not* take tyrosine supplements, and avoid foods containing tyrosine, as drug and dietary interactions can cause a sudden, dangerous rise in blood pressure. Discuss food and medicine limitations thoroughly with your health care provider or a qualified dietitian.

❑ Some preliminary studies show promise in using dehydroepiandrosterone (DHEA)—a hormone naturally produced by the body—in the treatment of depression. In one study, nearly all patients taking DHEA for six weeks significantly improved, and about half of those were no longer considered clinically depressed.

❑ Selenium has been shown to elevate mood and decrease anxiety. These effects were more noticeable in people who had lower levels of selenium in their diets to begin with.

❑ Vigorous exercise can be an effective antidote to bouts of depression. During exercise, the brain produces pain-killing chemicals called endorphins and enkephalins. Certain endorphins and other brain chemicals released in response to exercise also produce a natural "high." Most of those who exercise regularly say that they feel really good afterward. This may explain why exercise is the best way to get rid of depression.

❑ Music can have powerful effects on mood and may be useful in alleviating depression. (*See* MUSIC AND SOUND THERAPY in Part Three.)

❑ In one study, people suffering from depression were found to have lower than normal levels of folic acid in their blood than non-depressed individuals. Other studies have shown that zinc levels tend to be significantly lower than normal when people suffer from depression.

❑ It may be possible to diagnose depression by using a computerized tomography (CT) scan to measure a person's adrenal glands. Researchers at Duke University found that people suffering from clinical depression have larger adrenal glands than non-depressed people.

❑ A variety of different drugs are commonly prescribed to treat depression. Antidepressant drugs fight depression by changing the balance of neurotransmitters in the body. These medications include the following:

• *Monoamine oxidase (MAO) inhibitors.* These drugs increase the amounts of mood-enhancing neurotransmitters in the brain by blocking the action of the enzyme monoamine oxidase, which normally breaks them down. Examples of MAO inhibitors include isocarboxazid (Marplan), phenelzine (Nardil), and tranylcypromine (Parnate). Possi-ble side effects include agitation, elevated blood pressure, overstimulation, and changes in heart rate and rhythm. MAO inhibitors also have a high potential for dangerous interactions with other substances, including drugs and foods. Persons taking these drugs must adhere strictly to a diet that includes no foods containing the chemical tyramine, such as almonds, avocados, bananas, beef or chicken liver, beer, cheese (including cottage cheese), chocolate, coffee, fava beans, herring, meat tenderizer, peanuts, pickles, pineapples, pumpkin seeds, raisins, sausage, sesame seeds, sour cream, soy sauce, wine, yeast extracts (including brewer's yeast), yogurt, and other foods. In general, any high-protein food that has undergone aging, pickling, fermentation, or similar processes should be avoided. Over-the-counter cold and allergy remedies should also be avoided.

• *Tetracyclics.* These drugs have an action similar to that of the tricyclics, but have a slightly different chemical structure and appear to cause fewer side effects. Maprotiline (Ludiomil) is in this category.

• *Tricyclics.* These drugs work by inhibiting the uptake of the neurotransmitters serotonin, norepinephrine, and dopamine, making more of the mood-enhancing chemical messengers available to nerve cells. Examples include amitriptyline (Elavil, Endep), desipramine (Norpramin, Pertofrane), imipramine (Janimine, Tofranil), and nortriptyline (Aventyl, Pamelor). Possible side effects include blurred vision, constipation, dry mouth, irregular heartbeat, urine retention, and orthostatic hypotension, a severe drop in blood pressure upon sitting up or standing, which can lead to dizziness, falls, and fractures.

• *Other drugs.* Several drugs known as "second-generation" antidepressants have become available in the past few years. These new drugs have not been shown to be more effective than the others, but they tend to have fewer serious side effects. They include the newer tricyclic amoxapine (Asendin); fluoxetine (Prozac), paroxetine (Paxil), and sertraline (Zoloft), which specifically block the uptake of the neurotransmitter serotonin but, unlike tricyclics, not that of norepinephrine or dopamine; buproprion (Wellbutrin), which is believed to act by inhibiting the uptake of dopamine but not serotonin or norepinephrine; and trazodone (Desyrel), an antidepressant with stimulant properties that also inhibits the uptake of dopamine. One study done in Madrid, Spain, found that people who took fluoxetine, paroxetine and sertraline were three times more likely to develop gastrointestinal bleeding than those who did not.

❑ Steroid drugs and oral contraceptives may cause serotonin levels in the brain to drop.

❑ Prozac and other "selective serotonin uptake inhibitors" work to increase the activity of serotonin, while 5-hydroxytryptophan (5-HTP) works to boost the body's production of serotonin.

❑ A study published in *The British Medical Journal* indicates that extracts of St. John's wort may be as effective as prescription antidepressants for mild and moderate depression. St. John's wort is the most-prescribed antidepressant in Germany, but is treated as a dietary supplement in the United States (it is not approved as a safe and effective drug by the FDA). Many studies are underway to determine the effectiveness and safety of long-term use of St. John's wort, including a major study by the National Institutes of Health started in 1997.

❑ People who smoke are more likely than nonsmokers to be depressed. Smokers and non-smokers alike may benefit from Zyban (a sustained-release preparation of buproprion, also sold as Wellbutrin SR), an antidepressant also approved to help people quit smoking. Bupropion elevates levels of dopamine and norepinephrine, substances that are also elevated by nicotine in tobacco products. It allows patients to obtain the same feeling while weaning themselves off nicotine.

❑ Allergies, hypoglycemia, hypothyroidism, and/or malabsorption problems can cause or contribute to depression. In people with these conditions, vitamin B_{12} and folic acid are blocked from entering the system, which can lead to depression.

❑ Individuals with depression are more likely than other people to have various disturbances in calcium metabolism.

❑ There is no doubt that attitude affects health. Study after study has shown that optimistic people are not only happier but healthier. They suffer less illness, recover better from illness and surgery, and have stronger immune defenses.

❑ Many groups and organizations offer more information on depression (see HEALTH AND MEDICAL ORGANIZATIONS in Part Three).

Dermatitis

Dermatitis is a general term for any type of inflammation of the skin. Types of dermatitis include atopic dermatitis, nummular dermatitis, seborrheic dermatitis, irritant contact dermatitis, and allergic contact dermatitis. The distinction between the use of *dermatitis* and *eczema* to describe skin disorders can be confusing. Often, the terms are used interchangeably, although many people use the term *eczema* to refer specifically to atopic dermatitis. The inflammation of the skin that accompanies dermatitis (or eczema) produces scaling, flaking, thickening, weeping, crusting, color changes, and, often, itching.

Several underlying problems can lead to eczema. Hypochlorhydria (low levels of hydrochloric acid in the stomach) has been cited, as has a condition known as "leaky gut syndrome," in which the intestines become porous and allow particles of undigested food to enter the bloodstream,

provoking allergic reactions. Candidiasis (an overgrowth of yeast in the system), food allergies, and a genetically-based weakness in the enzyme delta-6-desaturase (which converts essential fatty acids into anti-inflammatory prostaglandins) are other possible causes of this condition.

Many cases of dermatitis are simply the result of allergies. This type of condition is called *allergic* or *contact dermatitis*. Skin inflammation may be linked to contact with perfumes, cosmetics, rubber, medicated creams and ointments, latex, plants such as poison ivy, and/or metals or metal alloys such as gold, silver, and nickel found in jewelry or zippers. Some people with dermatitis are sensitive to sunlight. Whatever the irritant, if the skin remains in constant contact with it, the dermatitis is likely to spread and become more severe. Stress, especially chronic tension, can cause or exacerbate dermatitis.

Atopic dermatitis (AD; also known as atopic eczema or, in children, infantile eczema) is a condition known to affect allergy-prone individuals. It typically appears on the face, in the bends of the elbows, and behind the knees, and is very itchy. In children, it usually appears in the first year of life, and almost always in the first five years. Over half of the infants who have this condition get better by the age of eighteen months. Triggers vary from person to person, but tend to include cold or hot weather, a dry atmosphere, exposure to allergens, stress, and infections such as colds. If other family members have histories of hay fever, asthma, or atopic dermatitis, it is more likely that a child will be diagnosed with AD.

Nummular ("coin-shaped") *dermatitis* is a chronic condition in which round, scaling lesions appear on the limbs. It may be caused by an allergy to nickel and is often associated with dry skin. *Dermatitis herpetiformis* is a very itchy type of dermatitis associated with intestinal and immune disorders. This form of dermatitis may be triggered by the consumption of dairy products and/or gluten. *Seborrhea* is a form of dermatitis that most commonly affects the scalp and/or face.

Unless otherwise specified, the dosages recommended here are for adults. For a child between the ages of twelve and seventeen, reduce the dose to three-quarters of the recommended amount. For a child between six and twelve, use one-half of the recommended dose, and for a child under the age of six, use one-quarter of the recommended amount.

NUTRIENTS

SUPPLEMENT	SUGGESTED DOSAGE	COMMENTS
Essential		
Betaine HCl	As directed on label.	A form of hydrochloric acid. People with dermatitis often have low levels of hydrochloric acid. *Caution:* Do not take this supplement if you suffer from stomach acidity.

Discovery Groups are for people of every race, religion, ideology and sexual orientation who seek to commune with others to expand their definition of Self, to heal from addiction, trauma, abuse, racism, sexism, to become more whole, and to develop a passion for all of life. The groups use the healing concepts developed by Charlotte Kasl to examine self-esteem, addiction and co-dependency in the context of internalized oppression. Her model is designed to empower individuals to find their own voices, sources of strength and spirituality.

Several copies of Kasl's "Healing from Trauma and Addiction with Love, Strength, and Power" will be available at the group for your use. There will also be books available for purchase at a reduced rate. For more information about Charlotte Kasl's l6-step model, please visit her website at www.charlottekaslcom/16-stepprogram.

If you are interested in attending the group or would like more information, please email the group - info@16steps.org. We are looking forward to this incredible opportunity to provide support and compassion for each other on our spiritual journeys to healing!

This group is not affiliated with AA, NA, or any other 12-Step program. Members and facilitators are at all stages in the "recovery" process, may still be struggling with addiction, and not expected to be held up as examples. We are all coming together in a common desire for health and happiness.

16 Steps for Discovery & Self-Empowerment
Group Guidelines
&OCß

Food & Beverages: Out of respect for those dealing with a variety of issues, please bring food or beverages for your own consumption. As a group we may organize events in which food & beverages can be provided with the group conscience in mind.

Start on time, end on time: If the group feels that the meeting needs to be extended, at the end of the meeting the group will make this decision. Those who cannot stay may leave; those who can stay are free to continue until an agreed upon time.

Focus on group purpose: Please remember that we are here to help each other become more self-empowered in dealing with addictive, unhealthy behaviors. We request that sharing be relevant to this overall group purpose.

Positive group energy, so no 12-step bashing please: People come to groups wanting to be inspired & to find healing. Any form of healing is good. Empowerment is about each finding our own way & respecting the paths of others. We acknowledge that there are those who have had negative 12-step experiences. Please feel free to meet with others outside of the group to process these experiences. Comparisons can be made during the meeting, as long as it is brief & we can move on.

Touching: Hugs, holding hands, etc., is acceptable only when given permission by the other person.

Confidentiality: As participants in this group, we are all sacred witnesses to each other's life paths. This is a gift that should be respected & valued & not taken lightly. We may talk about what we are learning in the group, but not about other people. What is heard here stays here. The level of trust in the group depends upon it.

"I" Statements are Best: When revealing your personal experiences, beliefs, & feelings, please use "I" statements.

No Cross Talk: While participants are sharing, please refrain from commenting. If the participant would like feedback, they will indicate this after sharing.

Feedback Optional: At the end of an individual's sharing, if he/she wants feedback, he/she may request it.

Avoid Advice Giving: This is a non-confrontational meeting, unless a person requests it, suggestions, direction, & confrontation should be avoided.

Responsibility: Everyone is responsible for his/her own feelings, needs, & wants. This means asking for what you need & want from the group & learning to voice your feelings & wants in a respectful way.

Respect: Each of us comes from different & unique experiences & places. It is hoped these differences will help us learn & grow. Each of us wishes to be respected & not judged. We may not agree with each other, but we need to respect each other for who we are right now.

Adults Only: Our discussions are adult-oriented & intended for people striving to maintain sobriety by discovering our inner worth & developing our personal empowerment. The group conscience has determined that it is in the best interest of everyone participating to have minimal distractions during the meetings to be able to focus our attention on our own healing paths. Therefore, we ask that participants please leave children at home. This is our time to find healing for ourselves, including those of us who are parents & caregivers.

16 Steps for Discovery & Self-Empowerment
Meeting Format
ଽ୦ଔ

Welcome
Introductions—Voluntary
Review of meeting format
Review of group guidelines
Chalice lighting

Reading
"We Gather Together & 16 Steps" (p. 58-59)

Step of the Week Exercise(s)
Personal sharing related to the step, or other sharing (2-3 minutes)
Ask for feedback if you wish (2-3 minutes)

Wrap-Up (10 minutes before end time)
Next Week: Same step or next step? Which exercise?
Announcements/Contribution reminder
Moment of reflection/silence

Closing: Group Reading (Group reads *italicized* print)

Now go in peace.
Salom & Shalom.
May you leave this place knowing you are good and knowing you are loved.
Blessed be.
Take your light and your love from this place.
Share them with the world and stay safe until we meet again.
Amen.

Extinguishing of Chalice

What Members of 16-step Empowerment Groups are Saying:

I cannot express my feelings on paper. Your books have given me validation and strength within myself I didn't know existed.
— Woman in Cincinnati, Ohio

"Dr. Kasl has written what thousands have felt for a long time. She has brought the field of addiction out of its complacent position in the dark ages and put it on the cutting edge of discovery."
— Nikki A. Mapley, President, Healing Fires, Inc. Arkansas

"The 16-step program encourages the voice inside of me to speak. It excites me like a kid in a candy store—I can choose whatever I want to do. I don't have to mouth words from the 1930s."
— Adam W., Minneapolis, Minnesota

"Attending the Women's Lodge [16-step] meetings has, more than any other single thing I've done, encouraged me to speak my truth, not just think it. As a result...I have been better able to speak with a strong voice and articulate my reality: "I see what I see, I know what I know, and I feel what I feel."
— Linda Nicita, Boulder, Colorado

"The 12-step program told me what I shouldn't do, the 16-step program tells me what I can do. The results have been amazing."
— Anne, Madison, Wisconsin

"As a writer and an artist, I value creativity in all of its forms: intellectual, visual, spiritual, emotional. This program has allowed me to value my "crazy" creativity. It has given me support to heal, room to grow, and an opportunity to meet the most wonderfully imaginable women who come from many (addictive) backgrounds, but thrive on an opportunity to discover their own creative, self-affirming road to unafraid, honest living."
— Sarah Massey-Warren,

"For 15 years I went to AA. When I tried to speak out on political issues or abusive relationships, I was always treated as if I was wrong, as if I wasn't going to maintain sobriety if I kept thinking and talking that way. I like the 16 step meeting I'm going to— it's a place to talk about whatever I want, to experiment, to be wrong, to take chances."
— Nance, Oakland, California

Responses to Charlotte Kasl's empowerment model as first presented in *Many Roads, One Journey: Moving Beyond the 12 Steps*.

"Dear Sister, Dear Friend, Dear Angel. Thank you for *Many Roads, One Journey*!!! I am feeling so energized, and empowered and hopeful after reading your book. You spoke to my experience. I felt mute, and you have given me words."
— Woman from Maine

"I think the 16 steps are wonderful! They give us a guideline to follow on the road to realizing the 'power' within."
        —An incarcerated woman in Ohio

I am very grateful you risked writing such a powerful book—for you, for me, and for our planet. I am 39, a successful African-American writer, teacher, bulimic, ACOA, co-dependent food addict—in recovery. I long to resolve my search for love and power in sex, men, and in pretending as if I'm white (middle class and educated). I took the steps to do so because I gained hope from your honest book."
        —African American writer

"*Many Roads, One Journey* must be one of the most important books I have ever read. The Internalized Oppression Syndrome describes my experience in life as well as my frustrations with Alcoholics Anonymous during eight-and-one-half years of recovery. In meetings dominated by certain types of sober men, sharing true feelings brought resounding criticism and shame-oriented attacks in front of the group.
        —58-year-old man

"It is refreshing to finally see someone take the risk of challenging the 12-Step philosophy. The majority of my caseload are multi-addicted women with childhood trauma issues. Your 16 Steps to Personal Empowerment have been extremely helpful to them."
        —A counselor with Lutheran Family Services of Nebraska

"Thank you !!! Thank you!!! Thank God for you!!! Your book *Many Roads, One Journey* made valid all the un-covery and discovery I've done as a gay man who left Al-anon many years ago."

"I am writing to thank you for your new book. It has been very popular and helpful in Marin County California where I direct a chemical dependency outpatient program."
        —Executive Director of Recovery Systems, Marin County, California

"As a man, I appreciate your evenhandedness in talking about the patriarchal system. You didn't say one harmful thing about men as individuals."

"I can hardly keep my enthusiasm to myself anymore. I've become very excited and hopeful after reading your book, *Many Roads, One Journey*. I had felt suicidal and crazy for three months. During that period I looked for something I could trust and believe in. I found that hope in your version of the steps. I was amazed how the slightest changes really made all the difference to me. I am now incorporating your 16 steps into my life. If there are any groups in my area using 16 Steps for Discovery and Empowerment, I would like to contact them."
        —Woman from New Jersey

"Thank you for sharing your truth. It is spiritually awakening for me. Your beliefs about addiction and internalized oppression help me feel empowered, un-crazy, un-unique. I am happy to be alive now with so much new to study and learn."
        —Woman from Newcastle, Maine

"When I read your chapter on codependency (re-framed as internalized oppression) I wanted to run to the highest mountain and scream as loud as I could, 'Yes! Yes! Yes!'"
—Woman from Lafayette, Louisiana

"I am setting up an uncovery/discovery group for HIV⁺ sex, love and relationship addicts. *Many Roads One Journey* has been most instrumental in understanding my initial and continuing ambiguity with SAA as a 12-step program. I took your book to an Intergroup meeting and everyone there wanted to get a copy so I know there is much dissension out there."
—Man from Texas.

"[As a result of reading your book] I am now hopeful and encouraged to continue my journey, trust in my own healing power, and look to find my true self. I told my therapist and psychiatrist about your book and gave them copies of the purpose statement and steps. I am starting a discussion group with others using your book and steps to guide us."
—A woman from Alaska

"Thanks for doing such important work."
—Board president, Wisconsin Coalition Against Sexual Assault.

"Thank you for saving me a year or two on my road to uncovery and discovery. I have been going to 12-step meetings for about one year. These meetings have helped me. However, I was increasingly troubled by the sin and redemption stuff due to the fact I went to 12 years of Catholic school. I was not allowed to voice my concerns in the sense that I was made to pay emotionally if I mentioned any doubts about the beloved 12 steps. *I want empowerment, not powerlessness.* I am sending you a photo of a cloud moving over a mountain near Banff, Alberta. It is a metaphor for what your new book did for me."
—Man from Wisconsin

"Your book was a real affirmation of my own journey and helped me to more fully come to terms with the tensions that I often feel inside of myself. *Stressing "powerlessness" to victims, as you say again and again, does little to help our healing and keeps us in the cycle of abuse.*"
—Man from Minnesota

"Thank you for writing your book and sharing yourself in this way with me. My road has been bumpy, dark and full of potholes. The work of people like yourself has illuminated the way and helped me to see my destination at a time when I couldn't see it myself!"
—Woman from Florida

ALSO BY CHARLOTTE KASL

Yes You Can!

***

*Healing from
Trauma and Addiction with
Love, Strength and Power*

With a New Section
**The Trauma-Addiction Connection:
Making Sense of Chaos**

by
Charlotte Sophia Kasl Ph.D

Based on the 16 Steps from
*Many Roads, One Journey:
Moving Beyond the 12 Steps and
Yes You Can, A Guide to Empowerment Groups*

To order copies of *Yes You Can!*
See web site www.charlottekasl.com
Or write to Many Roads, One Journey, P.O. Box 1302, Lolo, MT 59847
Groups and Bookstores call for special prices 406-273-6080

Logo on cover: Bird in Woman: Ancient Mimbres symbol of transformation

---

Library of Congress Cataloging-in-Publication Data
Kasl, Charlotte
    Yes, You Can! A Guide to Empowerment Groups (Based on the 16 Steps from *Many Roads, One Journey: Moving Beyond the 12 Steps*) 1st edition
    1. Empowerment   2. Addiction recovery   3. Self-help Groups
Library of Congress Catalog Number 94-094524
ISBN 0-9644520-0-6

"Written in the hope that people will adopt a life-loving spirituality that is passionate, powerful, loving, creative, and joyful—a spirituality that embraces all life as interrelated and sacred."

— Charlotte Kasl

Also to Sue

"Deep within us all there is an amazing inner sanctuary of the soul, a holy place, a Divine Center, a speaking Voice, to which we may continuously return."

— Thomas Kelly

<u>HELP US FORM A DIRECTORY</u>

If you know of groups, treatment programs, community agencies, or any organizations that use the 16-step empowerment model, *please let us know so we can create a directory*. Many people want to know where you are. Thanks.

<u>Send all relevant information, including a phone number to</u>:
Many Roads, One Journey
Box 1302
Lolo, MT 59847
or
office e-mail: <u>charlottekasl@yahoo.com</u>

ACKNOWLEDGMENTS

Throughout this project I have felt supported in a myriad of ways. I send cheers, courage and many thanks to all the people who have started 16-step empowerment groups, given personal support or arranged workshops in their area. You are the pioneers of this model and have helped many people with your dedication and hard work. Special thanks to members of 16-step groups who filled out my questionnaire for this guidebook, providing helpful suggestions and an abundance of quotes, which are listed before each of the 16 steps.

Heartfelt thanks to Pat Hanson, who gave me strong encouragement to write this guidebook, helped me organize the chapters, and provided many ideas for the exercises for each step. A bouquet of roses to Sandra Klippel, who started numerous groups in the Madison area and has worked to make many treatment programs and community agencies aware of this model. Best wishes and heartfelt thanks to Aikya Param, who formed a network in the Bay area around San Francisco, and contributed a valuable section on an empowerment approach to setting guidelines. Adam W. has been a dedicated supporter in the Minneapolis area. He helped start a group, formed a network and started the excellent *Empowerment News*, which you will see in the appendix.

Thanks also to Marceil Ten Eyck, who gave valuable input for the section on Fetal Alcohol Syndrome and Fetal Alcohol Effects. Thanks to Dawn Chase and Dave Cornell for their expert work formatting this guidebook and to Marga Lincoln for copy editing.

Warm thanks to my neighbors, loved ones and Friends of the Missoula Quaker meeting for all the joy, love and happiness you bring to my life. And finally, I want to acknowledge the spirit, joy and wonder I feel from the rivers, mountains, forests, and pine trees in this beautiful Bitterroot Valley, where I live.

Table of Contents

PART ONE

GETTING STARTED

Chapter 6: Maintaining Groups: Guidelines and Group Assessment

PART TWO
THE SIXTEEN STEPS: Readings and Exercises
NEW CHAPTER: The Trauma-Addiction Connection:
Making Sense of Chaos

Chapter 7: The 16 Steps

INTRODUCTION

Welcome!

At the core of everything I write and teach is the belief that true healing occurs through empowerment and love, not fear. In a culture so permeated with fear, it is important to examine everything we are told, and take only what affirms our intelligence, spirit and soul. I offer this guide as a self-affirming, wholistic, empowering model for groups and individuals. It can be used for overcoming addiction and for personal growth. Some people use the 16 steps in groups, others hang them on the wall to read once a day. Some people focus on one or two steps for long periods of time, others like to circle through the steps.

Since the publication of *Many Roads, One Journey: Moving Beyond the 12 Steps*, in June, 1992, hundreds of people have formed and participated in 16-step groups around the United States and Canada. This model has also made its way to Australia, New Zealand, England, Russia and Africa. I have been fascinated by the numerous letters I've received in response to the book and by the huge number of inquiries I get about the steps whenever they are mentioned in a magazine or article. In essence I have named what many people have been thinking or feeling, often in response to 12-step groups based on Alcoholics Anonymous. I have put words to a longing of many people to have groups that are flexible, socially conscious and affirming of peoples intelligence, creativity and capacity for wisdom.

Yes, You Can! is written in response to numerous requests for specific information on forming and maintaining 16-step groups. It stands on its own as a guide to groups and can be used along with *Many Roads, One Journey*. To gather materials for this guidebook, I went to the experts—the people who have started and maintained successful 16-step groups. They contributed formats, guidelines and stories of their experiences in the groups. More important, they talked about a subtle but profound shift they experienced after a few weeks or months in the group. "I felt stronger, more sure of myself, as if my voice were coming alive," one woman said. It is rewarding to hear these affirmations because I have a profound desire to see models of healing and empowerment that create whole, thoughtful, creative, fearless human beings who are not easy prey for propaganda and seduction, rather people who will question authority, speak up in the face of injustice, trust their inner wisdom and find happiness.

I originally wrote these steps in 1985 to answer a call within me that asked, 'what is it that will help me heal and become whole as a woman in this culture?" It soon became evident I was not alone on my quest. When I visit groups around the country and hear people reading these steps, I am reminded over and over that we are seldom alone with our thoughts and desires, and that the greatest power we have comes from speaking from our experience and our heart.

Like any model that questions tradition, suggests change, and honors individual differences, this approach has been met with fear responses. "How can you change something that works?" people will say. "Works for whom?" I respond. While 12-step groups have been life saving for countless people, there are millions more who have walked in the door of a 12-step meeting and said, "This doesn't fit for me." There are countless other people who have had tremendous help from 12-step groups, but felt they "hit a wall" and needed something more expansive and supportive, something that spoke of their culture, their politics, their individual needs.

In looking at any model of therapy or healing, we need to ask again and again: What are we trying to achieve with this model? Does it work? When does it work and when does it cease to work? How can we be respectful of each person's journey? How can a model reflect the needs of the people using it rather than imprisoning people with unexamined dogma and rhetoric? This model is designed to help people understand the profound impact oppression, racism and sexism have on our lives and provide a flexible, affirming, creative approach that helps people transcend addiction.

There is No One Way

It is up to each of us to listen to our heart, experiment with a variety of possibilities and choose whatever works for us. Words are only words. They are not sacred. The importance of words is to connect us to existing truths in a way that brings them alive for us and helps us heal and grow. What is sacred is the healing of all people. There is nothing sacrosanct about the model presented here. These steps are offered as a resource. Take them, use them, change them and make them your own.

Finally, please don't pressure another person to adopt this model, for that is completely contrary to the spirit of this book, which is to support all people in thinking for themselves and finding their own path. It is up to each person to choose whatever works for him or her. It is up to all of us to respect each other's ways.

Yes, You Can!

Charlotte Kasl

Lolo, Montana
January 13, 1995

CHAPTER 1

What is Empowerment?

Fundamentals of Empowerment

1. Empowerment is based on love, not fear

While fear may jumpstart people into recovery, only love heals. Fear of losing one's family, life, health or job may get a person started on the path, but only love and growth will keep a person going down the path. It is the desire for something better—a sense of wholeness, the ability to connect, freedom from fear, the desire for life, family and community—that brings powerful motivation to heal and become whole. It's hard to give up an addiction, but when there is a promise of something better, richer and more fulfilling, many find the courage to take that arduous journey.

When we affirm the power of love and allow the soul to dream, we become alive. This is a form of self-love and love of spirit because it opens us to all of our potential. An empowerment approach encourages people to break through limitations, enjoy their talents and strengths, use their rational mind as an ally in healing from addiction and bond in power and joy. Developing one's passions, finding purpose and strength and becoming involved in social change are seen as antidotes to addiction.

Opening ourselves to love can be bittersweet because when the love comes in we feel the age-old heartaches and rage we have buried. For many of us, addiction or depression has been the cover-up for pain—personal pain, and the pain of oppression to our people and our loved ones. Thus moving toward love means talking about our personal pain and the pain of our culture or community, which may go back for generations.

2. Empowerment is a wholistic approach to a problem

Healing and empowerment include body, mind, spirit and community. To overcome addiction or a sense of powerlessness people need to address all parts of their lives because ultimately everything is interconnected and interdependent. People may need to learn about good nutrition, avoiding harmful dependent relationships, developing assertiveness skills, and the impact of childhood abuse or internalized oppression on our lives.

3. Empowerment works toward transformation

In an empowerment model, addiction or negative behavior is seen as a form of energy. When we were hurt or afraid we put our creativity and energy into finding relief or escape. This may have formed patterns that led to addictions or dependent relationships. The energy underlying the addiction is not bad energy, it was a natural survival response. Transformation occurs when we take the energy that fueled the addiction and re-channel it to a higher purpose. The cleverness we developed seeking drugs can be used to find good therapy groups, jobs or good friends who support us in becoming healthy. Our fine tuned ability to sense other's needs, can be used to become aware of our own needs.

4. Empowerment is about choice

Because there is no one way all people grow and expand, we need different models to choose from. Growth is often a process of experimentation with different approaches that we test by reaching inside, listening to our internal wisdom and seeing what works. You can ask yourself: What feels right for me? What helps me feel less depressed? What helps me stay sober? What brings a sense of clarity and joy? Different approaches work for different people at different times. Empowerment helps us move away from fear because we take an experimental approach—we try something and if it works that's great, but if it doesn't work we don't judge ourselves; we simply say it didn't work and try something else.

5. Empowerment means living with complexity

Addictive thinking is often concrete and dualistic. It's very much the way young children think—things are right or wrong, good or bad. Healing from addiction and evolving into a mature human being means healing from addictive thinking—wanting quick fixes and simple answers. This means opening our minds to see complex problems and complex solutions and learning to tolerate the uneasiness of paradox and confusion. It means giving up pat answers and sometimes saying, I don't know. Or taking one step and only then finding the next step. It means experimentation, struggle and learning from mistakes. Thus healing becomes a process a bit like filling in the pieces of a mosaic—trying out this color and that, this shape and that, until the pieces fit together into a beautiful whole.

6. Empowerment supports flexibility and change

An empowerment approach includes being flexible to our needs as we grow and change. A certain approach may work for a while and then it no longer feels useful. Nothing in life is frozen in form. Everything is always changing. Part of becoming a whole, empowered person is to be receptive to the wisdom that comes from listening to those around us, taking in new information, paying attention to our experiences and tuning into our internal wisdom. This process helps us develop an internal center, or a sense of internal power from which we can take charge of our lives. A sense of self that is sturdy, flexible and rooted—like a willow tree—is crucial for staying in our own circle of power in the face of sudden impulses that could take us off course.

7. Empowerment encourages creativity

The more creative we are about the form we use for our healing, the more it lives within us. A starting place is to be creative with words. You can listen to the 16 steps and other models, and change the words until they connect with your heart, feel clear and powerful. By listening in this way you increase your consciousness and honor the mystical, magical person you are. Many people find that journaling, drawing, body movement, singing or writing create a mirror that helps them understand themselves. The more we live connected to our own wellspring of creativity and passion, the more alive we feel. And as we feel more alive, our motivation to stay clear of addictions becomes stronger.

8. Empowerment takes us beyond labels

We could all use many labels to describe ourselves—pianist, mother, father, creative, good reader, Native American, Jew, smart, dyslexic, Lutheran, addict, etc. I have great difficulty with people limiting themselves to the label addict, compulsive eater or codependent because too often people shrink themselves to fit their labels. It is important to validate all parts of ourselves and take note of our strengths because they are the building blocks of empowerment. We need to move beyond the concept of labels because they are not our core identity, and it is important not to judge ourselves or others based on labels. At our core we are part of all life and all life is sacred. Thus our labels dance around us, they are part of us, but they are not our core.

9. Empowerment teaches us to trust our wisdom

While we can all learn from books and other people, our ultimate source of wisdom lies within. We may have to grope in confusion, sometimes waiting to figure something out, but we need to trust that eventually, if we listen long enough, we will find our inner voice of wisdom. One way to access our inner voice is to ask repeatedly, What is best for me to do? What do I want? It may take a long time to develop the capacity to listen inwardly and trust what we hear, but we can start the process by adopting the belief that we are all the experts on our own lives and no one else can know what is best for us.

10. Healing is a community effort

People have a basic desire to belong to a group of people—to be accepted, valued and have unconditional support and love. It is magical to experience the transforming power of love and acceptance by a group of people committed to positive values. When a community creates norms of care for others, honest work, happiness, healing and empowerment, then people will naturally gravitate toward those values because it will bring a sense of belonging.

We heal to feel more power and joy in our personal lives, and we also heal to become a force for good. A vibrant, healthy person radiates healing energy to all around them and can be a powerful model for others in their community.

The Power of Groups

Groups are intrinsic to empowerment because instead of relying on experts, we learn through each other's experiences and come to trust in our own wisdom. Groups can ignite a powerful healing force. They can help to free the wisest part of each individual, resulting in a collective wisdom that is greater than the sum of its parts. An empowering group is where everyone pools their strengths to create a resource for all members to use—kind of like a lending library of inspiration and courage. Thus individuals who may not have enough personal strength to take a risk or meet a new challenge can borrow on the ego strength of the group to take a step in their own behalf.

When one person pushes through fear and takes a positive step, it sparks the will and power within other members. Examples of positive steps are standing up for oneself, getting out of a harmful relationship, going back to school, setting limits with friends, taking time for fun, and providing service to one's community.

One of the primary strengths of groups is learning we are not alone. As people's stories unfold we learn that others have experienced shame, fear, abuse, pain and loneliness…and everyone survived. A healthy group can help us learn basic trust. When people stick by us, listen to us, cheer for our growth and they don't go away when we make mistakes, tell our secrets, or show our tears, then we learn to count on others. And when we can reach out for others to comfort us in hard times and celebrate our successes together, we are less likely to reach for addictive substances or to become depressed or anxious.

Groups also have the power to be destructive. One example is when a charismatic leader attracts people seeking a substitute, all-knowing mother/father/God. The participants in the group deify the leader and absorb his or her will, becoming uncritically loyal and often violating their own values and betraying their own wisdom. An oppressive group can also be one based on a rigid doctrine that is not open to input, creativity or questions. People treat the doctrine or dogma as if it were a God and, again, stop thinking for themselves, growing, questioning or being creative. At the greatest extreme, groups are harmful when the leaders are adults taking advantage of the vulnerability of children for their own, self-centered needs. They use coercion, threats and manipulation to get the children to adopt a rigid belief system and take part in acts that are harmful and demeaning to them.

It is important that we create groups that are open to questioning, encourage creativity and help people come to know and trust their inner wisdom. This creates people who have a strong sense of self and are able to protect and care for themselves. People who have internalized their own sense of values are less likely to be seduced by propaganda, predatory people and slick political maneuvering. Because they have an inner sense of self, they are not easily hoodwinked. They feel more comfortable speaking their truths and taking a stand for what they believe in.

CHAPTER 2

Addiction, Healing and Relapse Prevention

Information is power. Knowing what stages we may pass through on the journey gives us the ability to reflect on ourselves and not get caught in fear and hopelessness when the going gets rough. Many of the concepts discussed here are explained at greater length in *Many Roads, One Journey; Moving Beyond the 12 Steps; Women Sex and Addiction: A Search For Love And Power;* and *Finding Joy: Freeing your Spirit, Dancing with Life*.

What is Addiction?

Addiction is an obsessive, escalating dependency on substances, people, sex, money, work or other behavior that becomes programmed into the survival part of the brain. It becomes a conditioned response to stress, fear, anxiety, loneliness or withdrawal. At a spiritual level, addiction is mistaking substances, things, status and people for gods. The survival part of the brain becomes programmed to believe that substances, people, sex, relationships, status, etc. will make us happy or relieve pain. It is a search for happiness and ecstasy gone astray because happiness comes from an internal journey to truth, love, service and a sense of connection to all life.

Common criteria for addiction are:

1. **Feeling powerless to stop at will** You say you are going to stop, but you can't seem to keep promises to yourself. You may stop for short periods of time and try to convince yourself you have control, but when you start again it's like an intruder into your life that starts taking over. Either the cravings or the longings overtake your good intentions.

5

2. **Harmful consequences either external or internal** External consequences can be poor work performance, car accidents, losing jobs, becoming violent, not paying the bills, stealing, breaking the law, etc. Internal consequences can be inability to concentrate, irritability, sudden shots of anger, loss of memory, depression, anxiety, loneliness, becoming emotionally numb or detached, or difficulty in intimate relationships. These are just a few of the many consequences that vary tremendously with different individuals.

3. **Escalation of use or dependency** The escalation can be physiological, as in the case with alcohol and other drugs as the body becomes more and more dependent on a substance. It can be behavioral, as in sex addiction—taking more risks, needing more partners, spending more and more time in a fantasy world, etc. Escalation can also become psychological as a person constantly reinforces the mind to believe that the only way to pleasure or the reduction of pain is through addictive behavior. This, in turn, results in depression and anxiety because it means moving away from one's true center.

4. **Unmanageability in other areas of life, either external or internal** Unmanageability manifests itself in a multitude of ways. For some people, chaos pervades their lives because they lose jobs, don't pay bills on time, are repeatedly sick, neglect their loved ones and children. Internally they become increasingly obsessed about their addiction, live in a state of fear or anxiety and become emotionally detached from others as the addiction pervades their inner world.

5. **Withdrawal upon quitting** Withdrawal can include intense cravings for the substance or person, obsessive thinking, anxiety, depression, fatigue, the shakes, heart palpitations, restlessness, sleep disturbances, fear, terror and cravings for substitute stimulants and depressants such as sugar, nicotine and caffeine.

From Re-covery to Un-covery and Dis-covery

In seeking words that fit with empowerment, I have used the terms un-covery and discovery that were originally coined by Mary Daly, a feminist theologian. To "recover" implies covering something over. To be empowered is to *uncover* the oppression that lives within us and then *discover* our authentic selves.

A common misconception of privileged thinking is that people who are depressed, addicted or in great emotional distress need to cast off their destructive thinking or behavior and return to a state that existed prior to their difficulties. For many people seeking to heal from emotional problems or addiction, there is not a whole lot to return to. They never had security, possessions, peace of mind and opportunities in their lives. So when they let go of the addiction or emotional problems, they will be faced with the awesome task of building a life. As Peter Bell, a chemical dependency counselor in Minneapolis said, "We're not re-habilitating people, we're habilitating people." One woman I spoke with who was recently out of prison and had been using the 16 steps, said "I've never seen myself as being a real person. Now I'm told I'm an addict. I don't want to see myself as an addict forever. I want to know about life and how to live because I've never had a life of my own."

Many Roads to Healing

Empowerment involves honoring and learning from different people's ways and then finding your own way. Some people give up drugs and alcohol on their own without formal treatment or attendance at support groups. Some may white knuckle sobriety and struggle with cravings for a long time while others lose the physical craving early on. Some people complete treatment and never attend support groups. Others go to support groups and never go to treatment. Some people go for help only after an intervention by others, while others realize for themselves that their addiction or destructive behavior is harming them.

Some people use Methadone or Antabuse as a deterrent to drug use. Others use a combination of 12-step groups and psychotherapy often for childhood abuse or neglect. Some people focus on re-connecting with their cultural roots or understanding the effects of oppression in their lives. Others get well by healing their physical body through good nutrition and exercise. People go to many types of groups such as Women for Sobriety, Rational Recovery, Secular Sobriety and 16-step empowerment groups.

Likewise people make all kinds of life changes in different ways. Some people come to new realizations through workshops, spiritual groups or books, while others use counseling. Some people put themselves in the same painful situation over and over again before they decide to change, while others learn quickly from experience and try other alternatives. One woman who left an empty marriage made a dramatic shift by repeatedly saying to herself, "I deserve more than that. I won't settle for less." She never had therapy, but by changing her beliefs she was able to change her life and find a warmer, more affirming partner. For most people, there is a combination of many forces at work that lead to change. Central to the whole process is an inner commitment we voice to ourselves—I am willing to do what it takes to change my life. I am willing to feel, I am willing to learn.

The Fear of Questioning

Some people experience intense fear when they think of trying an empowerment approach to healing. This is not surprising for three reasons. First, it asks that people reach inside for guidance and stop relying on external authority. Many people experience a flash of terror when they realize they are responsible for their life and there is no magic wand, no perfect person who can fill the inner void.

Second, our patriarchal, hierarchal culture is based on obedience and compliance with the status quo. Thus, when people start to think for themselves or take charge of their lives they feel as if they are breaking the rules or committing a crime against the powers that be.

The third reason people fear using an empowerment approach to heal from addiction is that they have often been told that the traditional 12-step Alcoholics Anonymous model is *the only way* to sobriety. Many people are grateful for sobriety and feel as if they owe their lives to 12-step groups. When something has been helpful, or we have been told repeatedly it is the only way, it can be hard to imagine that any other form could work. But, in reality, many forms have worked for many different people. I have spoken with hundreds of them.

Fear of change or trying a new approach can take the form of guilt, uneasiness, wanting to attack other people's ways, or hearing a voice in your head saying "you might get in trouble, be rejected," or "something terrible will happen." One woman at a workshop sat looking at the 16 steps and said, "I know I want something like this, but I have this feeling God will strike me dead for reading this." That's a natural response to being indoctrinated to a concept presented as "the truth" rather than as a belief system.

If you are afraid, you can say to yourself:

— It's natural to be afraid of trying something new, but I can still do it.
— I get to guide my own life.
— A lot of people make changes, I can too.
— I can experiment and decide for myself what works best for me.
— The voices of guilt and shame in my head were put there by other people. They are not genetic, and I can change them.

Defining Sobriety

Sobriety can take many forms depending on the addiction or dependency we are addressing. With drugs and alcohol, sobriety usually means abstinence. This is fairly easy to define. In general the first task is to dam up the flood of the addiction and contain it. But with time, as the addiction feels under control, we shift our focus toward growth, skill-building, friendships, relationships and community involvement. It is a process that unfolds over time moving us toward wholeness and happiness.

We can define sobriety in a broad context as well as in terms of addiction and dependency. Initial definitions of sobriety are often about *not* doing something: *not* drinking, *not* being seductive, *not* having anger outbursts, *not* shopping compulsively. While these can be important starting places, the concept of sober living can expand to include the things we do to feel whole, safe, healthy, expansive and happy.

Withdrawal from addiction sometimes includes feeling empty, dull and boring. Sobriety takes patience and the willingness to live through life's events staying connected to the feelings instead of escaping the discomfort.

Letting go of addictive behavior is a bit like digging up a bed of toxic weeds that spread and kill off all other plants, and then planting flower seeds. For a while the ground looks bare and empty, but eventually the flowers grow and are far more beautiful and healthy for the earth than the toxic weeds.

We can also talk about sobriety in terms of emotional problems such as depression, anxiety, or playing the victim. While depression and anxiety can have a physiological base that is relieved with medication, they can also be another form of escape related to lack of assertiveness or taking responsibility for one's life. Some people are extremely attached to a victim stance—the world is doing it to me. Sobriety from the victim role (which inevitably leads to depression) may mean giving up blame, no longer telling "what he/she *did to me* stories," not getting people to feel sorry for us, not keeping one's life in chronic chaos, not being sick all the time, not being overly busy and not getting attention through misery and pain. Or, translated to the positive, we recognize the harm that has been done to us, we name it, express our feelings, and take responsibility to make changes. We learn to take time for ourselves and say no to those who would drain our energy. We find people who are good to us, take action to have life less chaotic and dramatic, get exercise, eat in a way that promotes health, and bond with people in joy and power. Withdrawal from living in a victim stance (or what some people call codependency) often feels like committing a crime—the crime of breaking from symbiotic ties, giving birth to one's soul, and validating one's right to be here on this earth as a full-fledged member of the human race.

With addictions to food, sex and dependent relationships, the definition of sobriety is subtle, subjective and changes with time. With food, for example, we all need to eat, so sobriety will be about learning to listen to our body and asking, Why do I want to eat? Is it hunger? Restlessness? Fear? Anger? Some people will define sobriety as not eating white flour or sugar, others will define it as eating only when they are hungry and stopping when they are full. In another example, a woman who is sexually codependent might first define sobriety by no longer having sex when she doesn't want to. As her definition of sobriety expands, it might include taking care of herself in hundreds of ways by tuning into her body, asking for what she wants, saying no to things she doesn't want, and engaging in a long process of re-defining her sexuality on her terms.

For some people sobriety stops at containment of the addiction. They often keep the focus on the addiction and are constantly white-knuckling sobriety. A person may stay sober from drugs, but ingest lots of caffeine, nicotine and sugar; feel physically and emotionally drained and depressed; have troubled relationships and never feel at peace. Others, however, embark on a profound search for spirituality that includes major lifestyle changes encompassing work, exercise, relationships, nutrition, meditation, and community activism.

Internalized Oppression

At a personal level, internalized oppression is about all the voices that dance in your head stopping you from evolving into your wisest, most empowered self: I'm inferior; Be careful; Watch out; She might leave you if...; You might lose your job if...; It's hopeless, why try; I'm not worth it; I'm so messed up; I'm stupid, I'll never make it. These are all voices of oppression living inside you. The internal experience is like having two people inside struggling against each other—your authentic self trying to emerge and the oppressive voices trying to hold you back and keep you in "your place."

To explain internalized oppression: we live in a patriarchal system of variable worth. People are accorded privileges, respect and opportunity based on gender, color, class, ethnic background and sexual preference. A form of social control is to perpetuate these inequalities with limiting negative stereotypes. People are taught to absorb these damaging self-definitions and punishment is swift if you depart from your assigned role. The first level is verbal: for example, a woman who asserts her power is called a bitch, while a sensitive, emotional man is labeled a wimp or a queer. If verbal methods of control don't work, economic deprivation, violence, loss of jobs, lack of access to education, and various forms of harassment are used. It is often the resulting pain, alienation, poverty, and self-hatred that fuels addiction. Being lost in an addiction sometimes feels preferable to feeling unloved, rejected or without hope.

Internalized oppression is also about the false teachings of our society, namely that material goods make us happy and secure. In reality, too many possessions create fear and anxiety. People start hoarding things and wanting more and more because things never fill up the longing for spirit and connection to the earth. Our inner restlessness and need for constant stimulation are forms of internalized oppression. We have been trained to forget how to be at peace with simple pleasures. Our deepest level of internalized oppression is our attachment to our belief systems and our sense of arrogance about our superiority over other living beings. This includes our beliefs about using people and the earth as resources rather than as equal parts of a living web of creation that needs our care and respect.

Empowerment is about naming and recognizing negative beliefs you have internalized, casting them out, moving toward your authentic self and learning to live as part of the whole web of life. This can be frightening because it means questioning and challenging the limiting cultural stereotypes you have internalized and then taking charge of your life. I have long believed that it is a radical political act to become a whole, empowered, joyful human being in our society.

The Double Bind of Oppression

To understand oppression at a personal level, you can explore how you have been in various situations that created a double bind. The experience of a double bind is feeling trapped in a no-win situation. You're damned if you do and damned if you don't. There's a price to pay no matter what For example a parent may indicate to a daughter that she is lovable if she is sweet, docile and popular, although her nature is to be athletic, outspoken and have a few close friends. The double bind is that to be her true self—athletic and outspoken—she gives up her parent's approval, but to get her parent's approval she gives up her spirit and soul. Violence in the home creates a double bind for children. Do they experience the pain, or create a fantasy world where life is kind, or take control by blaming themselves? Do they learn to numb out, put on a tough exterior or lose themselves in sports, music, or being the perfect student while anger, fear and sadness gnaw away inside?

Rigid belief systems create a double bind. Do I go along with the crowd and have a stomachache, or do I speak up and risk being ostracized and shunned?

Other binds people commonly feel are: Do I stay in this mediocre relationship and keep the security, or do I leave and live with much less? Do I stay in the high paying job that is draining my life energy, or do I take a lower status job and have more time for myself and my life? Do I give up a low paying job that is draining me and go into debt to get trained for a better job?

Oppression leading to a double bind is related to sexism, racism, classism and homophobia. Some examples: Someone makes a sexist remark in your presence and you burn inside while you debate whether to say something and risk disapproval or keep quiet and burn away on the inside. You are given a book in school that does not validate your culture or heritage; do you speak up and be branded a troublemaker, or do you quietly acquiesce? Someone touches you in an icky way; you feel repelled inside, and feel a terrible conflict between saying something and making a scene, or going along and feeling sick inside.

Many of us feel a double bind related to our lifestyles: do we continue to exploit the earth's resources to maintain our lifestyles, or do we make substantial changes to live in balance with the earth's resources? While this may seem to depart from a discussion about addiction, I believe that it is core because at some level we all know that we are on a collision course with the destruction of our planet, yet our economic system continues to program people to maintain lifestyles that keep us on that course. This creates a tremendous double bind within us, whether we acknowledge it or not. And the tension from a double bind often leads to addictive behavior to cover our hopelessness, anxiety, depression and despair.

The double bind means that no matter how you respond, there will be positive and negative aspects. You either go along with the oppression and give up a part of yourself, or you react to the oppression and suffer the consequences. People often put themselves down for how they reacted to an oppressive situation: I should have spoken up or I should have kept my mouth shut. The important thing to remember is that either way you would have paid a price, so you chose whatever felt best at the moment. So instead of being hard on yourself, get mad at the oppression. (Three movies that illustrate the double bind of oppression are *The Milagro Bean Field Wars, The Power of One* and *Silkwood*.)

Here are some typical responses to oppression and oppressive teachings:
1. **Rebel, stand up for your beliefs.** The good part is that you hang onto yourself and your power. The negative part is that you are labeled a troublemaker and you lose access to rewards of the system. In addition, your peers may shun you because you are making trouble for them. At worst you are punished, imprisoned, killed or have your children taken away.

2. **Appear to go along with the oppressive teachings, but secretly hang on to your beliefs.** The positive aspects of this choice are that you get rewards from society, and you still hang on to a part of yourself. The negative part is that you live a dual existence, acting one way around the dominant group, and a different way around your peers. You might also be called manipulative or sneaky because

you change your behavior to fit in with different people. In reality, you are trying to survive.

3. **Buy into the value system of the dominant group and oppress yourself by believing what they say is true.** If you make this choice, you will be considered well adjusted and be rewarded by society. However, the cost to your internal world is tremendous. You are likely to become depressed, anxious and profoundly lonely because you have given up your self, your soul and internal wisdom, which is the source of spirituality. The complete form of internalized oppression is when you accept the harmful standards of the dominant group at an unconscious level and use them to oppress yourself and others like you.

    Paradoxically, when you make this choice, the oppressive people can then scoff at you for the very traits they said were desirable. For example, a woman takes on the stereotype of being kind, caring, sweet, passive, and deferring to others needs. When she gets depressed, she is told that she should be more assertive; when she wants to run for political office she is told she has been too passive, or she spent too much time at home with her children.

How does oppression connect to addiction? Oppression creates a double bind that produces chronic inner tension, particularly when you are not aware of the cause of the tension. People often put themselves down, feel crazy inside and blame themselves for the feelings. When there is no escape from a double bind, a person tends to seek a way to relieve the resulting tension. A quick and easy method is through addiction. Feel trapped? Drink, yell, space out, get depressed, eat, have sex, go buy something—anything to relieve the inner turmoil.

If you take a minute to think of all the ways you have been put in a double bind and how it has felt, you might start getting mad. That's good, because instead of thinking that you are crazy, you realize that the social system we live in is crazy. In a just society, people would not constantly be put in so many untenable situations where all solutions exact a terrible price. People ask, but wouldn't this be blaming? I believe that it is putting the responsibility where it belongs. Instead of individuals carrying the dysfunction of the society internally, they name the source. It's like accidentally taking poison, realizing it's making you sick and getting your stomach pumped to get it out. You name the poison as the cause of the stomachache and don't blame yourself. Getting angry at the double bind of oppression ignites our energy and actually frees us to take action—like cleaning the poison out of our system.

Blame is when we take no responsibility for our reactions to situations; we simply say, you made me do it, it's your fault. And then we take no steps to make changes. A first step to freedom is to recognize a double bind, name it, sort it out inside you and then make a decision based on full knowledge of the consequences.

Overcoming internalized oppression

To overcome internalized oppression the first step is to realize that the voices in your head are not true. They come from oppressive teachings that have made their way into your mind. They are impostors living inside you. You may feel crazy, but you are not crazy. You are not inherently manipulative, inferior or worthless, you have survived by acting manipulative, inferior or worthless.

If you do not undersand oppression, it can result in self-hatred and despair. If we think life is hopeless and we are worthless, then, well…why try. On the other hand, if we get mad and say, these lousy voices in my head don't belong to me, they've been put there, they are part of my oppression, I really am worthwhile, I can change, life can be better, then we are more likely to tolerate the discomfort of letting go of addiction and destructive behavior.

Healing from addiction, therefore, needs to incorporate an understanding of domination, subordination, socialization, and internal oppression. I believe everyone who is struggling with addiction, needs to ask: am I abusing this substance or being addictive or dependent as a form of self-hatred or despair, rather than being angry at a culture, system, or persons who have abused or oppressed me?

The Positive Intention of Addiction and Dependency

In an empowerment model, addiction is not seen as the enemy, rather as a survival mechanism that was often triggered in childhood. Neglected? Eat for comfort, become invisible, masturbate. Abused or battered? Use drugs, alcohol, anything to numb the pain. Want to feel important? Deal drugs, seduce someone. Afraid you can't survive without a partner? Hide your power and acquiesce to dull or repulsive sex. To survive, we may have withdrawn from people, been rebellious, or taken on the role of the perfect, super competent person—good, helpful or charming—always looking to help others. These roles we adopted led to loneliness, isolation or to unhappy, abusive or violent relationships.

One task of healing from addiction is to validate the positive survival goals of comfort, pleasure, love and power underlying the addiction, then find non-addictive ways to meet those needs. People talk about a drug of choice, but we could also talk about the addiction of choice or the escape of choice—the way that worked best to feel pleasure, or at least bring the momentary relief from pain.

It is crucial to remember that the addicted part within us is frequently an extension of the "wounded child" within who desires love, care and protection. Feeling little or needy became "bad," so we discovered indirect methods for meeting our needs. Ultimately, healing will include a re-integration of the child within who was doing his or her best to survive. For this reason shaming the addicted part of oneself can be ineffective or harmful. To transform addiction, you learn to reach under the addict part to the child and embrace the underlying struggle to survive: I understand why you ate all those cookies—they felt sweet and filled you up after being abused. I understand why you joined a gang, You wanted to belong and have friends. I understand why you went along with a man and did illegal things or got into prostitution, you were longing for someone to take care of you. Then you elicit the adult part of you and teach the child new ways: I won't put you down for having done that, but I am going to teach you new ways to find love, sweetness and personal power—ways that don't cost you so dearly. (A process of integration called "I Understand" is included with the handouts in the Appendix on page 117.)

Relapse and Slips: Remembering and Forgetting

Relapse is typically defined as giving up on sobriety and returning to addictive use of alcohol, other drugs, food, sex or work. Or it is not taking care of ourselves in a way that leads to depression, anxiety and dependent relationships. The definition of a relapse varies with different addictions, but harmful consequences are sure to follow. At its deepest level, it is a sense of inner collapse, a loss of spirit, hope and faith.

Slips are when a person, in spite of a commitment to healing, uses or reverts to addictive behavior on a one time basis or for a short period of time. Slips are not *caused by* external events—they are caused by the permission-giving statements we make, but we put ourselves at high risk for a slip when we let ourselves get overwhelmed. Slips can be related to getting overwhelmed due to death, loss, rejection, or other stressful events. Slips are also more likely when people fail to nurture themselves on a daily basis, isolate, or fail to ask for help with a crisis. Sometimes the desire to use happens when a person begins to face childhood abuse issues and becomes overwhelmed by painful feelings. A slip can be used as a wake-up call, alerting you to pay closer attention to your process of healing and your feelings.

In therapy I tend to spend less time talking about the actual slip than talking about the preceding cues that suggested the person was shutting down emotionally, not taking care of daily tasks, not dealing with feelings, not being honest, or not avoiding overly stressful situations and relationships. I also have the person examine the ways they started giving themselves permission to use: *Just once won't hurt.* It is important to stress that a slip is not the same as a relapse, nor does it necessarily lead to relapse. Many people grow and heal in spite of having slips along the way. On the other hand, some people who have never made a firm commitment to sobriety use slips as an excuse for continued use, saying, "It's just a slip."

A slip does not erase the days of sobriety that preceded it. You can never take away a sober day. Some people think they have to start counting the days and months of sobriety all over if they relapse or have a slip. I think it is important to say the whole truth: "I stayed sober for two years, then I had a slip, and I've been sober for four years since then." It all counts.

In my experience it is important to take sobriety very seriously. Once you have erected the wall between you and your addictive substance or behavior, your survival brain starts learning other coping mechanisms to create pleasure and cope with stress. When you have a slip, your brain once again gets the message that drugs, sex, violence, etc. are ways to alleviate pain. Once the barrier is down, it takes time to erect it again. It's like building trust in yourself again. One woman said that in her treatment program, which stressed sobriety very strongly, few people had slips and nearly everyone maintained sobriety. In another program which was loose about slips, more people had slips and relapsed back into their addiction.

It's a fine line because you can get so obsessed with sobriety you get frozen in your life, on the other hand if you continually allow yourself slips, you are also frozen in your life. Essentially, it's good to do all you can to avoid slips and relapse. And if you do slip, it's important to have a positive attitude, get back on track and keep going.

In defining sobriety it is important not to get caught up extensively with clock time and calendar time. It is important to look at quality as well as quantity of sober time, although all sobriety is good. If a person stays sober for eight years but is still being violent and abusive, what does that mean in terms of human life? If a person is growing and healing and has a slip, what has that small slip erased? If a person abstains from drugs but is eating compulsively and is depressed, what does sobriety mean for that person? The point is for the whole person to be growing, stretching and healing...as well as maintaining sobriety.

Dry drunk

Most people will have ups and downs in the process of uncovering from addiction or letting go of self-destructive behavior. When you take off a protective shield, you will usually find pain, anger or hurt underneath. Some people use the term dry drunk. A dry drunk is staying sober, but feeling lousy, afraid, disconnected and unhappy. You may wonder in these moments if sobriety is worth the trouble. (It is!) Dry drunks can be caused by underlying feelings coming to the surface that were buried underneath the addiction. It can be because we are not facing painful issues in our lives such as a battering relationship or a job we hate. Another cause of dry drunks is from living in a body that is physically out of balance. Our bodies are like an ecological system and abusing drugs or food, or living under severe stress can leave us physically depleted, which affects our brain chemistry and our moods. The main thing is to know that you can do things to alleviate the discomfort—get nutritional counseling, improve your diet, and exercise. One addiction counselor said that people are prone to dry drunks at three, six, and nine months and at the first year. If people know this is a common cycle, they won't be so alarmed by the feelings.

While the term dry drunk is helpful to many, I have mixed feelings about it because it seems inaccurate. The person is not drunk, they are sober and feeling fear, depression, withdrawal, or trying to repress underlying pain. It seems more accurate to describe what is going on and affirm that the person has maintained sobriety even though he or she is struggling internally.

Five-Stage Addiction Cycle

In order to explain relapse as a cycle, we need to examine addiction or return to self-destructive behavior as a cycle. This cycle can be broken down into five parts: fleeting idea, mental attention, obsession/planning, using and guilt/remorse. The cycle usually starts with some kind of blow to the ego that feels painful or overwhelming. The survival brain immediately seeks relief, pleasure or comfort.

Here are the stages:

1. **A fleeting idea.** First, there is a fleeting/harmful idea—an image of the addictive behavior. This can be the thought: wouldn't a drink/chocolate taste good right now? I really need to see Jeffrey again. It often feels as if the thought entered from outside oneself.

2. **Toying with the fantasy.** Second, our addict part gives the fantasy willing attention and toys with the idea. Like playing with fire, there can be a high attached to the sense of danger. The addicted person cons him or herself with a permission giving statement: Oh, just this once; I can always quit again; I can control it; No big deal. A person starts imagining that first drink, going to the race track, or seeing an old lover. In response to these thoughts, the brain chemistry changes, creating a sense of relief or a "high." The addictive trance is taking hold. Many people describe experiencing a "click" as they move into the addictive trance.

3. **Making plans.** The third stage is full-fledged obsessing and making plans for the addictive acting out. The adrenaline starts to flow with anticipated pleasure or relief from tension as the person becomes preoccupied with the euphoria that will come. You disconnect at a deeper level from the present. This is a time when accidents happen, people misplace things, or totally tune out conversations: Oh my God, what did he say I was supposed to do.

4. **Acting out the addiction.** The fourth stage is engaging in the addictive behavior and feeling the momentary release. It can be the high that comes with the first drink of the day, making a sexual conquest, going to the Bingo parlor, or going to see someone you were trying to stay away from. For a little while you feel better, but sooner or later you pay a price.

5. **Hangover.** The fifth stage is when the reality of life dawns and once again the underlying loneliness and sadness along with remorse or shame for acting out the addiction are felt. You feel emptiness and terror as you realize, perhaps for only a moment, that you can't find love in a bottle, at the bottom of a pack of cigarettes or in a wild sexual encounter. The hangover may trigger a period of "being good" and making resolutions, but eventually, if the underlying feelings are not addressed or the person doesn't have skills for staying sober, or does not break out of the shame cycle, something will again trigger the addictive cycle.

How to Break the Five Stage Addiction Cycle and Prevent Relapse

It is helpful for people on a healing path to spend time learning these stages and then personalize them by identifying their own behavior that corresponds to the different stages. These stages can be applied to addiction, dependent behavior, violent behavior, depressive thinking, anything that takes you away from your good and caring self.

Here's what you can do:

1. **Learn the cues** that trigger your addiction(s). Cues can be people, smells, music, places, parties, certain magazines and so on. The accompanying feelings can be loneliness, panic, emptiness, shame or guilt.

2. **List the fleeting ideas** that tend to come into your head that are the addictive side tempting you: Wouldn't a drink taste good right now?

3. **List thoughts** that counteract toying with an addictive idea: This is dangerous, I'm playing with fire. I'd better quit right now and call someone.

4. **Make a list** of your permission-giving statements: Just once; or I'll quit tomorrow.

5. **Make a list of all the reasons** to stay sober or on your healing path. Hang this list where you can see it or carry it with you...or both: My family, health, self-respect.

6. **Make a list of all the self-talk** that helps you to stay sober: I can stand this craving; it will pass; I don't ever want to go through withdrawal again; the cost is too high.

7. **Make a list of people you can call** who will be helpful. (I underscore *helpful* to your *sober* side.) Put this list up and carry a copy with you.

8. **Imagine your healthy side** co-opting the cleverness and power of the addictive side and using it to sabotage the addictive impulses. Take yourself to a support group, to the movies or call a friend.

9. **If all fails, and you have a slip, be nice to yourself,** learn from your mistake, renew your commitment to yourself and your sobriety, and go on.

10. **If you outwit your addictive side,** feel high from taking care of yourself. Get your friends to cheer for you and celebrate with you.

The above is a safety net when you are falling into an addictive trance. At a deeper level, relapse prevention comes from taking wonderful care of yourself—talking to friends, staying in the present, learning, growing, clearing out pain from childhood, igniting a passion for life, developing assertiveness skills, having fun, developing your strengths and learning to talk to yourself in positive ways. It is also important to stay connected to your feelings and connected to other people. *Addiction thrives in isolation.* Maintaining a connection to yourself and others is part of the antidote to addiction. The other is telling yourself repeatedly you can stay sober no matter what.

In short, make a plan, stay aware, be true to yourself, stay with reality, and keep at it. The more you stay sober, the better you will feel. Keep telling yourself you know what is good for you, you know what will help you maintain sobriety and you know what will help you grow. Then go to a group and find friends who support you on the journey.

CHAPTER 3

Fetal Alcohol Syndrome and Fetal Alcohol Effects (FAS/FAE)

The Relevance of Understanding FAS/FAE for People in Recovery/Discovery

FAE and FAS are emotionally laden yet important subjects that are often neglected in "recovery" circles. Some people who attend recovery/discovery groups for all forms of addictions and dependent relationships have been affected by FAS or FAE. Either their mother was using drugs (including alcohol) during pregnancy or the individual in recovery/discovery used or abused alcohol or other drugs during pregnancy and affected their children.

In a brochure by the Montana Fetal Alcohol Syndrome/Effects (FAS/FAE) Program, the common behavior profile in FAS/FAE is: Extremely active, easily distracted, impulsive, poor judgment, poor communication, problems with transitions, hard time keeping friends, socially engaging, interested in others, affectionate, loving, talkative, good with animals, makes friends easily. Diane B. Malbin, has a detailed list of learning problems in her excellent article: *Learning and Behavioral Characteristics Associated with FAS/FAE which May Reflect Organizity and Secondary Symptoms which May Develop Over Time.* Some of the learning problems include translating information from one modality to another. For example: Seeing into writing, thinking into speaking, feeling into talking, hearing instructions into carrying out instructions. Other difficulties can be in generalizing, conceptualizing, abstracting, seeing similarities and differences, sequencing, prioritizing, organizing, structuring, initiating, following through and retaining and utilizing information. The effects can be blatant or they can be subtle. They can vary from day to day. I urge anyone who suspects they may have learning or emotional problems related to FAS or FAE to get a copy of her fine article. You can write her: Diane B. Malbin, M.S.W. FAS/FAE Counseling

19

and Consultation, 15500 N.W. Ferry Road, PO Box L-14, Portland, OR 97231-1331
Phone/Fax 503-621-1271

It is crucial that people with suspected FAE or FAS have an evaluation. Without the proper diagnosis, people often don't get appropriate help. Many people are being treated for a tiny piece of the problem, but not getting the overall help they need. This is important for drug/alcoholism counselors, social workers and psychologists to understand. If a brain problem (organicity) is being treated as a psychological problem, the person will waste time, feel more frustration and shame, and the therapist will not be of help. For the person with FAE and FAS there is often great relief in getting the diagnosis: "Oh, I'm not crazy." "It's not my fault. I'm not stupid. There are reasons for what I go through." Following a diagnosis, you can embark on finding the right strategies for that person.

It is also important that counselors and staff in treatment programs understand the implications of FAE and FAS, because many of their clients may need help for emotional and learning difficulties that stem from organicity and not emotional or family problems. Because people with FAS/FAE have difficulty translating information into action, programs that are based on teaching the consequences of alcoholism and other drug abuse, may be ineffectual. That doesn't mean there isn't a way to help people with FAE or FAS, it means there needs to be consultation with a learning specialist to learn methods that will connect internally and work for people with FAE or FAS.

To the Mothers of Children with FAS and FAE

One of the most painful emotional tasks you can be handed is to acknowledge that your drinking or other drug use affected your child's (or childrens') development and brain functioning. Mothers speak of the intense grief and shame they feel as they watch their children struggle in a multitude of ways, and realize their drug use was the cause. A woman named Marceil Ten Eyck (formerly Vadheim) writes in "Iceberg," an educational newsletter of FAS and FAE, "When I first heard about fetal alcohol syndrome, a cold, sick feeling lodged in the pit of my stomach.... However, I was able to convince myself that Sidney's small size, her immaturity, her difficulty with memory and her extremely short attention span were due to her prematurity...and the stress of my divorce." This illustrates the inner conflict women experience when they start to realize their child's problems may be related to their drinking/drug use during pregnancy. One would rather attribute the problems to anything other than one's own drinking/drug use.

If you do not allow yourself to accept and face the truth, you won't go through a process of grieving and healing crucial to your spiritual and emotional health. Also your child may have more severe problems because he or she doesn't get the proper diagnosis. This will cause extreme stress for yourself as well as your child. It may seem like a paradox, but the more you can let go of your guilt and shame, the more you can be of help to your child. While you need to go through a grieving process, your self-forgiveness will free both you and your child. Children feel the burden of a guilt-ridden parent and then focus on helping the parent instead to putting their energy into their own survival. You can be a model for your child of someone who has met a tough situation with grace, dignity and courage.

I underscore that you don't have to walk this path alone. There are other women you can talk to who will understand what you are going through. It won't be easy, but it will lead to a path of healing for you and your child. Staying guilty will not help your child. People with compassion and understanding can give you the support and help for working with your child. Marceil Ten Eyck is a therapist in private practice and has an office located at 1029 Market Street, Suite C2, Kirkland WA, 98033. Phone: 206-827-1773. She is willing and ready to provide inservice trainings or workshops to any agency or group that would like to learn more about FAS/FAE. She is also willing to talk with mothers whose children have FAE/FAS. Another resource is Antonia Rathbun, 909 S.W. St. Clair, Portland Oregon 97205, Phone 503-292-2346. She has written an excellent article including sections on *Common Reactions [for parents], Receiving a Diagnosis, Techniques for Professionals Working with FAS/ FAE* and *FAE/FAS in the Classroom.* One final resource is Debra L. Evenson's article, *Integrated Active Learning and the Child with FAS/FAE: Help for Tired Teachers.* She is in Homer, Alaska. Her warm optimistic approach is extremely helpful.

Basic Understanding of FAS/FAE

1. While there are diagnostic criteria for FAE and FAS, no single picture fits all people with FAE/FAS. Some will read better than others, some will learn math better than others. Some people have great difficulty making friends, others make friends easily. Some have difficulty holding down a job, others are extremely dependable on a job. Some may have great musical talent, others may not. Just as all people are different, so are people with FAE and FAS. It is important to always relate to the person/spirit and not make assumptions about learning and social skills without checking them out.

2. If a child has FAE or FAS, many problems that appear to be behavioral may be related to developmental delays or neurologic impairment. Some children with FAE or FAS are mistakenly diagnosed with Attention Deficit Disorder (ADD), or hyperactive when this is a symptom of a bigger problem. Treating an isolated part often sets the child up to fail and may set up a cycle of emotional and behavioral failure patterns that are harmful to the affected person, the family and the community.

3. Many children not properly diagnosed with FAE and FAS have problems relating with other children, appear to be uncooperative, defiant or oppositional, and get suspended from school, mocked or shamed as a result of adults not understanding the cause of their behavior. For example with FAE or FAS, a child can hear words and directions and repeat them back perfectly, but have no idea how to put them into operation. They can be told to take off their coat and hang it up. They can repeat back the statement, agree to do it, and then drop the coat on the floor, smile

and walk away. That's because the brain circuits don't hook up to move from words to behavior. Often adults mistakenly think the child is being defiant; they start yelling and punishing. However the child actually wanted to cooperate but needed to be shown how to hang up their coat. This is but one small example of how a neurological problem can easily become a behavioral problem when not understood.

4. Many people with FAE and FAS build up enormous energy and frustration in school or at work when trying to perform tasks. To drain off this excess energy that sometimes feels explosive, people with FAS or FAE might move their arms or legs rapidly, tap, move in their chair, or get up and take a quick walk. When this is not understood and encouraged, as it should be, children (or adults) are seen as uncooperative or difficult. They are actually trying very hard to take care of themselves so they can function appropriately. If they can be encouraged to release pent up frustration, their ability to perform can increase and they feel understood.

5. Many people with FAE and FAS have "good days and bad days" meaning that one day they can grasp something and do it well, and on the next day, they can't understand it at all. Again this is often misinterpreted as being uncooperative or willfully defiant. People with FAE and FAS talk about feeling as if there is a wall in their head. They know the information is there, but they just can't get to it. The circuits don't seem to connect. Another common experience is instant short-term memory loss. The child is told to pick up a toy, starts walking over to do it and then can't remember what he or she was told. If this is misunderstood as defiance and the child is punished, it creates shame and often develops into low self-esteem and emotional problems that could have been prevented.

6. Children (and adults) with FAE and FAS are often able to show teachers or others how they experience their learning process through drawings and art work. This helps teachers, parents and therapists understand the internal experience of the person with FAS/FAE and can lead to a joint effort to find creative solutions. Children and adults with FAE and FAS often learn in kinesthetic ways through the use of color coding systems or being shown how to do things behaviorally. They often have creative areas where they excel and this can be encouraged.

7. In traditional 12-step recovery groups, such as Alcoholics Anonymous or Adult Children of Alcoholics, many traits listed as symptomatic could result from FAS/FAE rather than a "dysfunctional" family. Some of the traits are difficulty in relationships, difficulty initiating projects, rigidity, need for immediate gratification, depression, forgetting, explosive anger, frustration, relationship problems, difficulty learning, etc. If there was alcohol or other drug use during pregnancy, people need to ask, What if some of these behaviors are also related to FAS or FAE? Maybe the solution isn't simply to attend support groups and have psychotherapy. Maybe it has to do with problems in the brain. Maybe there is help with learning styles that could be of much more help.

Author's Personal Note

As someone who struggled with undiagnosed dyslexia until I was in my late thirties, I can attest in some small way to the frustration one feels when one's brain doesn't work well, and you don't understand why. Until I was diagnosed, I always thought that a part of me was stupid. One of my symptoms was difficulty organizing things to go somewhere. As a young child, I would be trying to get papers and school books together and things would drop all over the floor and I would feel tremendously anxious. My father, who taught statistics called it the Charlotte Distribution. Although he didn't mean to hurt me, this created tremendous shame and anxiety, because I obviously couldn't do what other kids seemed to do easily. As an adult, just getting organized to go to work out at a gym and keep my stuff organized made me feel like a total klutz. Other people could come in, change, and get to their work out while I was still trying to "get it together" just to be dressed, take what I wanted with me, and leave the rest in the locker without having everything spilled all over the floor.

The dyslexia affected me throughout my education. Even though I appeared intelligent in school in many ways, I could never finish a multiple-choice test because those types of questions sent my brain reeling. My experience reading multiple-choice test questions (along with college sociology/psychology texts) could range from the feeling of energy circuits misfiring, to total confusion, to exhaustion and my brain going to mush or becoming blank. I have vivid memories of taking tests and watching all the other students get up and hand them in when I was only half way through. I'd think to myself, I know so-and-so isn't that much smarter than me, what's wrong with me? I can still see various teachers trying to pull a test away from me while I was hanging on to it pleading for "just a little more time." Over the years the anxiety around tests slowed me down even more.

In college I continued to cope by asking professors in advance what kinds of tests they gave. If it was multiple-choice I didn't take the course. In all the times I talked to professors and explained I couldn't finish multiple-choice tests, no one ever suggested there was a learning problem. I was given special dispensation to be allowed into graduate school because my Miller Analogy test was so low. I couldn't finish the test because my mind went blank for about half the time. I was allowed into the counseling program because I had taken several courses in advance of applying for admission and had all A's. What confusion and shame. Why couldn't I do those tests other people did so easily?

The sad part of this is the useless suffering; there are many ways to compensate for dyslexia. I needed to know I had dyslexia, be told I wasn't stupid, and to be validated for the ways I had learned to manage—drawing little diagrams and pictures on the margins of tests or books to help the words make sense. The other major (and simple) solution was to give me more time. Once I knew about the dyslexia (the year before I took my psychology boards) and could ask for more time, my anxiety went down, I could concentrate better when I studied, and with double the time I could perform quite well on tests. If I hadn't been diagnosed, I never could have passed the psychology boards, become a psychologist, written my books, or followed my calling in life.

You would not be reading this book right now. While my learning disability was minor in comparison to many, you can see how it spilled into so many areas of my life and career, affecting my self-esteem and my ability to follow my chosen path. Multiply this 10, 20 or 50 times over and you may understand some of the problems a person with FAE or FAS lives with on a daily basis and how important it is to have an accurate diagnosis.

For a newsletter on FAS/FAE called FASETS, or for more information you can call 1-800-447-6614 or 406-444-7530 (Shodair Hospital) or write to FASETS, c/o B. O'Hara, Shodair, P.O. Box 5539, Helena MT, 59604.

CHAPTER 4

Forming Groups

Notes From Successful Groups

I talked with people who started or joined 16-step groups in order to find out what made groups successful and what caused groups to fall apart. Some clear patterns emerged for the successful groups: Here they are... and *please let me know if you have any other suggestions.*

What Makes a Successful Group?

1. **Structure.** When you don't have a leader, you need structure to hold a group together. This includes a format and group guidelines that should be available to new members so they will know what to expect. Some people feel rebellious at having structure because it reminds them of authoritarian, bureaucratic, rigid thinking. The purpose of form and structure is to embrace the group with a safety net so people have clear boundaries and expectations. Guidelines and structure are there to serve the good of the group, not to become a prison or to block an individual's growth.

2. **Starting promptly.** *It's very important to start on time and end on time.* It gives a group stability. Even if two people are there, start on time. People tend to like something they can count on. The idea is to set an example of clear boundaries and responsibility to members, rather than bending the group to accommodate people who are late. When a group keeps starting later and later, people start second guessing when to show up and it creates confusion. One group said that they would sometimes run over, but at the scheduled time to end they would contract about how long they would go over.

3. **Consistency.** Once a format and meeting place are decided on, stick to them for a while, or make only needed changes. Constant change will effect people both

consciously and unconsciously—particularly if they come from chaotic families. They may not even know why they feel resistant to coming, but they know they don't feel safe. A steady routine provides a sense of security and safety. This, in turn, helps people feel free to talk and open up. Consistency doesn't need to mean rigidity. There can be flexibility within the format. For example a different person can bring a closing of their choice each week.

4. **Follow-through.** After the organizational meeting, it's important to get started with regular meetings as soon as possible. Most people will be fine with one or two organizational meetings to decide on structure and guidelines. Beyond that, people tend to feel exhausted by processing and drift away. In general, you can set a structure and see how it works. It's better to get started with something than to drag the organizational meetings on and on and get too complicated. Nothing will be perfect and you can make changes along the way.

5. **Keep the energy positive (no 12-step bashing).** People come to groups wanting to be inspired and to find a healing place. It's important to bond through sharing strengths and giving support to each other. I have heard from people whose groups engaged in 12-step bashing/criticism. It created negative energy and drove people away. *I ask that you do not put down any form of healing in a 16-step group. Empowerment is about each person finding his or her own way and respecting the paths of others.* While many people come to 16-step groups because they have had negative experiences in 12-step groups, others come who feel deeply grateful to their 12-step meeting yet want to explore something more empowering or different. In any case, those walking into a group and hearing a lot of negative energy about 12-step groups or anything else, may feel they won't be respected and accepted.

I discussed this issue at length with many people in 16-step groups and people who have left 12-step groups. For people who have had harmful or painful experience in 12-step groups, it may be important to get together with others to talk about it. There is also a process of letting go and grieving for people who have had good experiences in 12-step groups, but have decided it feels right to leave. Like dealing with any transition, you can mark it by talking about it, saying goodbye and opening the door to new experiences. While it is important for people to create a safe place to express these feelings, I strongly urge that they do this *outside* of a 16-step group. I know how natural it is to want to compare, but done over a long period of time it will harm the group.

At the same time you need not be rigid. People who have felt empowered by the 16 steps naturally want to express gratitude and speak of the differences they experience between the groups. If this is done briefly and then people move on, that's fine. But if people use the group to repeatedly vent negative feelings, it will drag the group down. Often the people who come in and use a lot of group time venting their anger, leave the group when they are through, and the regular members are left feeling empty because they didn't talk or get connected.

When participating in a 16-step meeting at a woman's music festival attended by women from all over the country, I heard women express gratitude for this new model. But as they started to compare and put down the 12-steps, you could feel the energy in the room go down. Then a woman said, "I am so much wanting the visitors here to have an experience of a true 16-step meeting, so I would ask that we stick to discussing these steps." When the group agreed to do so, the energy in the room shifted and felt much better.

6. **Define group composition.** It is fine to have certain generic types of groups so long as it doesn't result in making judgments of individuals. Examples that worked:

    1. All womens groups
    2. All mens groups
    3. Groups for a particular addiction
    4. Groups for all addictions but for one gender
    5. Second phase recovery/discovery groups.
    6. Groups for empowerment and growth (no addiction required!)
    7. Closed groups. This was most often a group at a church that started a discussion circle, or a group of colleagues who decided to have a group for themselves.

    If you are going to have an open group that is advertised, then all people mentioned in the advertisement should be welcome. Some have raised the question of having a "phase two group" for those who have their sobriety under control and want to focus on growth. It is fine to advertise or announce a "phase two group," but beyond that *it is not all right to exclude anyone who comes.* People must be allowed to decide for themselves. Otherwise groups can seem like cliques, and people will feel excluded or harmed on a personal level.

    Many people wrote to me saying that they attended both 12-step and 16-step groups simultaneously. It worked fine for them, and I encourage people to do whatever feels right. Some people have joined Secular Sobriety Groups after reading about them in *Many Roads, One Journey*. That's good too. All healing is good.

7. **Protect the group process.** I have heard of many groups that were working quite well, until a new person came in, monopolized the time, broke the boundary rules or was inappropriate in other ways. Others sat quietly and let it happen, or withdrew from the group, and the group fell apart. (This is reminiscent of families where the sickest person has all the control, and everyone sits around quietly seething, hurting and withdrawing.)

    Members need to take responsibility to protect their group. It's a given that life will hand us difficult people on occasion. Groups will find it a challenge to be kind and respectful, yet maintain the group process so it serves the needs of all the members—the way a healthy family functions.

If a person comes in with a big crisis, don't jump in to fix the crisis and interrupt the flow of the group. It is important not to reinforce people for getting into a crisis. Instead give attention to those taking care of themselves. If people want to help the person in crisis after the group meeting, that's fine. You might want to keep in mind however, that many people have learned that the only way to get attention is to be in crisis or portray themselves as victims.

Even though it is difficult to set limits, it is good modeling not to allow people to gain power by pulling others into their chaos. The group can get excellent practice in assertiveness, and the one in severe distress can learn the group's boundaries and limitations. In Toughlove support groups, for example, people are told they are not to take extensive time the first week. This prevents people from dropping in when they have a crisis, using all the group energy, and then disappearing— until the next crisis. A support group is not a therapy group and is not designed to handle chronic crises. As a therapist I've noticed that when I cheer for people who are taking care of themselves, and don't reinforce crises by giving them undue attention, people stop having so many of them.

8.   **Group guidelines.** Most successful groups develop a set of guidelines to make the group safe and consistent. It can help immeasurably to hand these guidelines out to newcomers so they have an idea of what to expect and don't feel hurt and embarrassed by being told either directly or indirectly they did it wrong. Some groups read the guidelines whenever there is a new person. Others read them every week. Still others read them when anyone asks to have them read.

9.   **Graceful endings.** Don't spend a lot of time trying to stop someone from leaving. People instinctively know if a group is within their comfort zone. Recognizing your feelings, but don't shame people for leaving. If possible, support them in making the decision that feels best for them. Wish them well and get back to your own work. If you are the one leaving, let the group know you are going *without blaming the group.* If the group wants genuine feedback they can ask, "Is there some particular reason you are leaving *this* group?" The person may have some helpful suggestions, such as needing more structure or wanting positive energy. If you are the one leaving, just acknowledge that you need to leave—it's not a fit, you want something else—and do so without blaming. It's your choice.

10. **Group assessment and reflection.** Group strength depends on the group's ability to respond to the needs of its members. Groups evolve and grow just like people. It's important to stop and ask, "How are we doing?" or "What do we need to keep this group alive and responsive for the members?" At the same time, don't make processing the central focus of a group. Processing is crucial, yet it can also get in the way of the primary function of the group, which is to provide a healing, empowering circle for people.

How People Started Groups

Here are some of the ways groups got started, or people convinced treatment programs to let them use the 16 steps.

1. A counselor, Sandra, started a 16-step group for people who were chemically dependent or partners of addicted people. She got the group listed at a prevention center, but later noticed they had dropped it from the list. When she asked the staff why, they responded they had decided the 16 steps were "too advanced." She told them, "People are staying sober in these groups who could never stay sober in 12-step groups…and they're doing it without treatment programs." The prevention center put the 16-step group back on their list. Moral of the story: assume all things are possible and be persistent.

2. A group of people in a church started a discussion group on *Many Roads, One Journey* and later turned it into a 16-step group.

3. A women left a mixed 12-step group to start an all women's group that did not do very well. She changed it to an empowerment/discovery group open to all people with all forms of addiction. She got an excellent turn out, and there are now three groups in her town.

4. Someone brought the 16 steps to their 12-step CODA group. Some people wanted to use them and others didn't. The 16-step advocates broke off and formed their own group.

5. A women's therapy center made their building available to people who wanted to start a group and helped them by announcing it in their newsletter.

6. One group decided to use the 12 steps one week and the 16 steps on alternate weeks. Another group read both the 12 steps and the 16 steps every week.

7. One woman walked into a treatment program carrying *Many Roads, One Journey* and a copy of the 16 steps and said, "I want to use these in the treatment program." They said okay.

8. One woman who was in a public treatment program said to her counselor, "Now I want to get sober but I can't relate to 12-step groups—I've tried—you have to help me find something else. "Her counselor didn't know what to do and said, "Maybe you would be happier in another treatment program." She replied, "This is a public treatment program and I'm the public, now treat me." About a week later, the counselor accepted that the woman really didn't want to use the 12 steps; she opened her bottom drawer and pulled out a copy of the 16 steps and *Many Roads, One Journey.*

9. A therapist started two therapy groups using the 16 steps combined with a group process. One group typified phase one—maintaining sobriety—and the other was a phase two group. They would discuss a step a week. Partici-

pants would keep a journal and open the next meeting talking about insights they had gained throughout the week. Then they would discuss the next step.

10. A teacher in a high school for recovering chemically dependent adolescents took the 16 steps to her staff. They used them for their own consciousness raising to look at their attitudes toward power and empowerment. The treatment programs that referred students were uneasy about using an empowerment model, so the teacher introduced the 16-steps class that looked at all forms of healing from addiction.

NOTE: I have heard from counselors in numerous treatment programs who have been instructed to first try and convince people to use the 12 steps (and not mention other programs). Then, if the person has a relapse, or keeps arguing or just "can't relate" to the 12 steps, the counsellor is allowed to mention the 16-step model, Women for Sobriety or other recovery groups, (although they rarely have a list of where these groups meet). Some counselors and staff psychologists and psychiatrists have let people know about *Many Roads, One Journey* and the 16 steps, sometimes in secret because it goes against the policy of their program. So if you are going to attend a treatment program, you might ask about their policy. If you want to use the 16 steps, persevere. There's no guarantee it will work out, but what do you have to lose? It also paves the way for the next person who feels as you do. Sometimes it takes a few people saying the same things for others to hear it.

Therapy Groups and the 16 Steps

I have spoken with several therapists who used these 16 steps as a foundation for therapy groups which included a fee. Several report having excellent results. Some used each step for two weeks, taking an hour to talk about a step and an hour for personal work. Others did a step a week and had people pick out one or two steps they particularly wanted to work on over a long period of time. It is all right if therapists use these steps in groups, *but it doesn't mean I endorse the group*. I have no control over the skill of the therapist or that person's ability to communicate the fundamentals of empowerment. It is up to those attending a group to decide if the group is good for them. Even if you love the steps, it doesn't mean the group is right for you. On the other hand, even if you are not wild about these steps, with a skilled therapist, the group might be beneficial. It's up to you to decide.

Outreach

Adam W. of Minneapolis said that one of the most important aspects of a good group is outreach. I agree. The more you make your group known, the more people will come, and the more you will build a solid core group. That is what gives a group a sense of stability and security. Personal referrals from therapists, addiction counselors, psychologists and other professionals can be very helpful. This may take some phone calls, visits to people, and mailings, but if possible it is well worth the time. It's a wonderful service to let others know you exist. There are a lot of people wanting 16-step groups.

I strongly urge you to have a copy of the 16 steps and the introduction to meetings when you contact professionals or get articles in the paper. I also suggest you include the 16 steps in articles and flyers because the steps speak for themselves. They are powerful in attracting new members. If you meet with people you can also show them a copy of *Many Roads, One Journey* and/or this guidebook.

Ways to Advertise or Let People Know About Groups

1. Local recovery newsletters—insert an announcement or write an article
   Several newsletters have printed the 16 steps
2. Women's psychology newsletters
3. Women's centers, lesbian organizations
4. Men's centers
5. In newspapers that have free listings of support groups
   List it weekly
6. Make posters and put them up around town—libraries, bookstores, co-ops
7. Talk to counselors in treatment programs
8. Church bulletins
9. Listing on cable television, computer bulletin boards, the Internet
10. Submit articles on the 16-step process in professional journals, recovery newsletters, newspapers
11. Put a notice on a national computer bulletin board on *America Online*, *Compuserve*, or some connection to the Internet.
12. Be creative and come up with your own outreach ideas

Networking 16-step groups

There is a great need for a national network for 16-step groups. I get numerous calls from people around the country wanting a group or a treatment program. Developing a national network starts with community networking.

Here are things you can do on a local level to help the process:

NOTE: *Give a copy of the 16 Steps to everyone you contact.*

1. Call a local self-help clearinghouse in your area. (A list is in the appendix on page 129.) They are committed to helping people start and maintain self-help groups. If you have a group, give them all the relevant information. If you want a group, ask them if they would be willing to keep your name and give it to anyone else who calls wanting a group.

2. If you have a group, get it listed with a local help line. These are sometimes called "First call for help" or a "help line" and are often listed in the front of a phone book. Take some time to explain about the group. Send them a list of the 16 steps and the introduction. If you have a group, give them all the relevant information. If you want a 16-step group, ask them if they would be willing to keep your name and give it to anyone else who calls wanting a group.

3. If there are several groups in your area, have a get-together. Some groups have had a potluck and watched the video I made on empowerment groups. Others have gotten together and talked about their experience and had a social hour.

4. If there are several groups, start a simple newsletter. A wonderful one from Adam W. of Minneapolis is included in the appendix on pages 114 and 115.

5. If you have a group, list it weekly in a local newspaper. Many have a free announcement column. There are often a lot of small papers and recovery newsletters. Get it listed in as many places as possible.

6. Make an appointment to talk about the model with counselors or administrators of treatment programs, shelters, prisons and half-way houses of all sorts. Particularly emphasize any good results for yourself.

7. If a few members of a group agree, ask to do an in-service at a local organization such as shelter, prison or half-way house.

8. Write a letter to the producers of the Oprah Winfrey show or other shows that will give this national publicity. A list of addresses is in the appendix on page 130.

9. Sponsor a workshop. Many communities had an upsurge in 16-step groups after I presented a workshop/training on empowerment and overcoming addiction. Workshops are usually arranged through community hospitals, mental health clinics or by small groups of people. In the process of arranging the workshops, sponsors often talk with staff from other agencies. While many are resistant at first, quite a few come to the workshop and leave with a positive feeling about the 16-step approach. One woman in Madison, Wisconsin, was able to get over 30 sponsors for a workshop and that created a huge network of organizations familiar with the 16-step model.

CHAPTER 5

Organizing a Group

The Organizational Meeting

Once you have decided to form a group, set a time for an organizational meeting. If some of these instructions seem obvious or simple minded, my experience in leading groups for 20 years has taught me that attention to detail pays off. Remember, most people resist something new or live under a lot of stress. The easier you make it for them to get to the meeting, the more likely they are to come. For example, if directions are vague, it's easy to turn on the TV and stay home. If there's no one to phone as a contact person, some people may feel too uneasy to show up at a strange place all alone.

The Announcement (see examples p. 35-37)

1. List the time and place.
2. If possible have the phone number of a contact person on the announcement.
3. Give detailed instructions on how to get to the meeting place. Maps help.
4. Say who the group is for, e.g., all men, all women, all addictions.

The Room

1. Find a central place that is easy to get to. Keep in mind public transportation if that is relevant for your area.
2. Find a comfortable room with pleasant lighting. Many people struggle with depression and dim rooms don't help. Others are sensitive to very bright lights. However, many wonderfully helpful groups have met in tacky church basement lounges with terrible lighting!
3. On the meeting day, put signs on the front door and in the hall directing people to the room. (People's anxiety levels rise as they wander around a building, feeling lost while searching for a room.)

Other preparation:

1. Prepare an agenda for the meeting and have a few core people there. If you are a committee of one, know that others have started groups all on their own.
2. Set a time limit, probably 1 1/2 to 2 hours, no more.
3. Have a facilitator who can keep the meeting on track.
4. Have copies of the 16 steps and the opening *We Gather Together*. You might bring copies of this guidebook and/or *Many Roads, One Journey*.
5. Have a place available for future meetings. *Once you convene a group and get the energy together, you don't want to lose it.*

The following pages contain sample announcements for 16-step groups. You are welcome to use the format or wording for your group announcement.

16-STEP

EMPOWERMENT SUPPORT GROUPS

CHICO, CALIFORNIA

Join others in a weekly self-supporting group based on Charlotte Kasl, Ph.D.'s work in her books: *Many Roads, One Journey: Moving Beyond the Twelve Steps, Women, Sex and Addiction: A Search for Love,* and *Power and Finding Joy: Freeing Your Spirit and Dancing with Life.* Regardless of what issue you wish to work on, this support group will provide a safe, structured environment to become more whole, develop a passion for all of life, and learn techniques for transcending low self-esteem. Ongoing, come anytime. Self-supporting, based on weekly contributions.

When:
    <u>Tuesdays:</u> 3:30 *(Men & Women)* - Butte College:
      Campus Library. Room 330. *Melody: 899-9570*

    <u>Tuesdays:</u> 7:30 *(Women Only)*
      Trinity United Methodist Church-Chico
      5th & Flume *Cynthia: 895-1670*

    <u>Wednesdays:</u> 5:30 *(Women Only)*
      Paradise Church of Religious Science
      Billie Road (left off Skyway) *Pat: 872-3966*

    <u>Thursdays:</u> 8-9 a.m. *(For Mental Health Professionals.)*
      St. John's Episcopal Church Floral (South of East)
      Barbara: 891-3667 : Julie : 891-0639

    <u>Fridays:</u> 5:30 p.m. *(Women Only)*
      Church of Religious Science
      14 Hillary Lane (left off Cohasset at Burnap)
      Chico, CA *Peg: 893-4246*

PATH OF WOMEN

EMBRACING

RECOVERY

POWER

You are invited to become part of the collective wisdom and healing force of Path of Women Embracing Recovery, a women's support group. We are in the process of healing and understanding issues of self-esteem, addiction and co-dependency.

We are using the healing concepts developed by Charlotte Davis Kasl, Ph.D., as outlined in her book - *Many Roads, One Journey*. Dr. Kasl provides help for women who have become uncomfortable with the traditional focus on conformity, humility, and personal failings. Instead, she examines self-esteem, addiction and co-dependency in the context of internalized oppression. Her model is designed to empower women to find their own voices, sources of strength and spirituality.

Tuesdays 7:00-8:30PM

The Women's Recovery Center
311 Mapleton Avenue
Boulder, Colorado
The 2nd Floor Adolescent Hospital Day Group Room

A RECOVERY / DISCOVERY GROUP FOR WOMEN

A group for women of every race, religion, ideology and sexual preference who seek to commune with other women, to expand their definition of Self, to heal from addiction, abuse, racism, sexism and patriarchy, to recover their wholeness, and to discover their bliss.

We are a group of women, some seeking new alternatives to traditional twelve-step programs, some seeking new paths of feminine expression, all willing to face our fears and celebrate our strengths. We incorporate ritual, meditation, prayer, play and Charlotte Davis Kasl's 16 steps for Discovery and Empowerment into our format. We are also open to suggestion and change—flexibility is more important than form.

If you're interested, or just curious, please join us and see for yourself.

The only requirement for membership is that you *be a woman.*

Monday 8:00 PM to 9:30 PM
At the Cosmic Cup, 2912 Oaklawn Avenue
Dallas, Texas

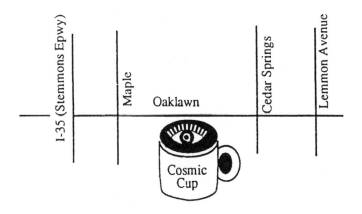

For more information call Gretchen at 826-9948 or Robin at 218-5233.

16-Step
Women's Sobriety
Meeting

Tuesdays, 5:30 p.m.

St. Luke's Episcopal Church Library
46th St. and Colfax Ave. S.
Minneapolis

Contact: Sheila 824-3023

This group is for those desiring a safe and affirming place to share their experience, strength, and hope for living with freedom from addiction. The group format makes use of the 16 steps which go beyond the 12 steps and focus on empowerment and wholeness, encourages one to seek power and guidance for personal recovery from within, acknowledges oppression, and honors differences.

Format for an Organizational Meeting

The suggested format below combines input from several groups. Remember, there is no one way, and it doesn't have to go perfectly in order to get a group started. Sometimes we have a plan, and it works fine. Other times we need to change it mid-stream because of the group "personality." So take what you like, create your own way and have a good time.

1. **Introductions.** What brought people to this meeting, what do they want the potential group to be or provide? NOTE: Figure out how much time people can talk and still leave time for organization. If you have 10 people and want 30 minutes for introductions, say that each person has three minutes to talk, and have a time keeper. Without it, some people are likely to talk much longer, and you won't have time for the rest of the agenda.

2. **Present the agenda for the meeting.**

3. **Reaffirm the composition of the group.** Decide if the group is all men, women, lesbian, gay, mixed?

4. **Reaffirm the focus of the group:** Is it for a particular addiction? For all addictions? For anyone wanting an empowerment group? Open? A boundary group (as defined on page 40, #11).

5. **Hand out the 16 steps and** the introductory page, *Many Roads, One Journey, We Gather Together.*

6. **Hand out suggested formats** or have them on a large piece of paper where everyone can see. Discuss them. If possible, decide on a group format.

7. **Announce the possible options for meeting spaces.** Have the group decide on a time and place. If attenders know of other places, they could be discussed as well. *If at all possible have the next meeting set up by the close of the organizational meeting.*

8. **Ask people if they have any questions or concerns.** Note: try to include discussion of people's concerns. However, don't let the meeting get too far off track. The facilitator can decide if various concerns are central to the first meeting, or if it would be better to discuss them later.

9. **Pass around a sign-up list for names and phone numbers.** (If possible, run off copies at the meeting and give a copy to everyone. If not, encourage people to get each other's phone numbers.)

10. **Pass the hat for money if there is a fee for the room.** If a fee was not mentioned in the announcement, it should be completely voluntary.

11. **Make a list of anything that needs to go on the agenda** for the next meeting.

12. **Decide on the facilitator for the next meeting.**

13. Do a closing.

Possible closings:
— Each person could go around and say one or two words (literally) about how they feel at the moment.
— The facilitator or people who organized the meeting could have a written closing.
— The facilitator could ask the group what they'd like to do, and someone could come up with a suggestion.
— Say good-bye and leave.

Other Organizational Concerns

Here are some other issues that you may want to address. You may want to include them in the first meeting or at a later date, or never.

1. **Time keeping.** Do you want a time keeper or do you want people to take responsibility for themselves? In some groups this is not a problem because people are conscious of leaving time for others, in other groups it becomes a problem because some people don't notice the time when they are talking.

2. **Develop a language to keep the group on track.** For example, members could agree to interrupt if someone is going on at length and say, "I'm aware of the time, and others still need to talk." Someone could be timekeeper, or mention when there is 15 minutes of group time left. People could also develop a language to remind people not to give advice or cross talk.

3. **Decide on a moderator/facilitator** to say, "Let's start now, let's end now." (What name do you want to use for the moderator/facilitator/secretary/trusted servant?) How often do you want to rotate, or do you want to let it unfold? Have a plan for alternating so no one person is seen as a leader.

4. **Develop guidelines.** (See Chapter 6)

5. **Discuss making contacts** with treatment programs, therapists, churches, people on the Internet and relevant newsletters to announce future meetings.

6. **Find out which people are willing to be contact persons.**

7. **If there are dues, have someone volunteer as a treasurer.** Discuss how the dues should be spent.

8. **Decide on confidentiality guidelines.**

9. **Decide if you want to ask for a six week (more or less) starting commitment** for new members. While this can't be rigidly enforced, a lot of groups do it to help people get through early ambivalence about attending a group.

10. **Discuss policies on touching and hugging.**

11. **Discuss the possibility of being a "boundary group."** Sometimes a group has a number of people who have confidentiality issues with other people in their community. This could be therapists who do not want to have clients walk in, other professionals who do not want to have their clients walk in, or people who don't want a former lover/partner to come in by surprise. Some groups have a policy that if you want to join, you send your name to a contact person. The name is taken to the group, and if someone has an objection based on confidentiality problems, the person is kindly told to find another group. This can not be done lightly and should only apply in clear cases of boundary problems. While some people do not like this policy, it protects the confidentiality of people in public positions and those who want to have one private, safe place for themselves.

Formats for 16-step Meetings

Here are some ideas for formats, including two examples from successful groups. As mentioned earlier, groups with a clear format that is followed regularly are more likely to attract people and keep them coming back.

1. Opening Possibilities

— Everyone goes around and says their name and anything they want to say about themselves: "I'm Ed and I'm addicted to alcohol and here to stay sober and grow." "I'm Allanda and I'm here to become a powerful woman. "I'm June and I'm working to eat in a self-loving way." "I'm Andy and I'm here to overcome addictive sexual relationships." People can decide to respond "Hi Jan," or just have people introduce themselves.

— A one-minute check-in of what went well that week, what each person has done to take care of themself. (This can be very effective and set a positive tone.)

— Someone does a meditation or reading that affirms the group in some way.

— The group decides on a reading (for example one group used the Quaker quote in the introduction to *Many Roads, One Journey*).

2. Introduction to the 16 steps

— Read *We Gather Together*, or some other opening, or a version of *We Gather Together*.

— Go around and read the 16 steps, with each person reading one or two.

— Read the discussion of the step included in this guidebook or in *Many Roads, One Journey.*

— Have someone "lead" by telling what that step means to them. (People can volunteer the week before, so they come prepared.)

— Have people discuss how they relate to that step in their lives.

3. Closing Possibilities

— Have a person read a quote, something that is personally meaningful. You might have a couple of books handy (*Earth Poems,* for example) in case someone forgets to bring something. Rotate, so each week one person reads a selection.

— Say the serenity prayer.

— Have everyone say a word about how they are feeling.

— Have a moment of silence and then yell, "Good for us."

— Have a moment of silence with the understanding that anyone can say a few words if they so desire.

NOTE If you close with a circle or hold hands, make it clear that people can choose *not* to hold hands, and *not* to be in a group hug. Let people say what level of contact they want. This protects people from doing something that doesn't feel right because they want to fit in (a double bind!).

Examples of Group Formats

The following pages have samples of group formats from Chico, California, and Dallas, Texas. (These are slight modifications from the originals). You can use them as they are or as a springboard to find what works for you.

SAMPLE FORMAT
From Chico, California

1. **Welcome.** *Pass around suggested guidelines. A moderator will start the meeting with a reading of the preamble,* We Gather Together *and all 16 steps in turn by participants.*

2. **Feelings check in.** *One-minute introductions followed by a statement of how that person is doing today.*

3. **Step reading.** *A step a week is read aloud by group members from* Many Roads, One Journey *(p. 340-356). When appropriate, the section contrasting this step with the traditional twelve steps is also read (p. 308-327).*

4. **Personal Sharing.** *Try to keep under 5-7 minutes. Group members will introduce themselves and respond to how they relate to the step reading of the week. See* Many Roads, One Journey *for written exercises. Sometimes we spend more than one week on a certain step. Persons sharing can ask for feedback if they wish. Feedback may be limited to two minutes.*

5. **Contributions.** *A treasurer will collect self-supporting contributions, and see to it that the site gets a donation at the end of each month. Monies may also be spent for xeroxing copies of the steps and meeting notices.*

6. **Phone list.** *A phone list will be passed around twice for voluntary listing of names and numbers.*

7. **A moderator** *will watch the clock, letting participants know when there is about 15 minutes left, so those who still wish to share may. A summary of the themes reflecting what group members discovered may be discussed.*

8. **Closing.** *Hold hands. Have a moment of silence. (Variation: hold hands, and out of the silence say one or two words about how you feel at the moment.)*

THE WOMEN'S LODGE IN DALLAS, TEXAS
FORMAT FOR A 16-STEP GROUP

1. **Open with a ritual** to create a circle, draw people together, and honor the space and the women who meet there. (optional)
   a. **Make any announcements** and call for announcements from the group
   b. **Acknowledge newcomers,** if any
   c. **Explain sequence of meeting:** that we will read a preamble, there will be a 10-15 minute meditation, then a topic will be introduced and the rest of the meeting will be devoted to voluntary sharing.
   d. **State that the group has elected to have a "no cross-talk" rule:** this means that people are requested not to speak directly to or about another person in the group while sharing. In practice this means sharing about one's own experiences, feelings, etc., and not addressing someone else's.

2. **Read preamble and sixteen steps**

3. a. **Begin meditation** (10-15 minutes)
   b. **Close meditation** with a gentle reminder that time is up.

4. **Introduce topic** (one of the 16 steps or another appropriate topic), remembering to state that people may talk about whatever they need to. If there are newcomers present, an appropriate topic may be, "How do you define your sobriety today?" or one of the first four steps.

5. a. **15 minutes before the end of the meeting,** announce the time
   b. **Call for $1 donations** for cost of space and materials.

6. **At close of the meeting,** have someone read an abridged version of *The Sabbath of Mutual Respect* by Marge Piercy or another selection (optional)

7. **Close meeting with a song** (choose one)
   1. We all come from the Goddess
      and to her we shall return'
      like a drop of rain
      flowing to the ocean

   2. Oh Great Spirit
      earth, sun, sky and sea,
      You are inside
      and all around me

   3. Listen, listen, listen to my heart's song
      Listen, listen, listen to my heart's song
      I will never forget you, I will never forsake you
      I will never forget you, I will never forsake you

   4. The river she is flowing, flowing, and glowing,
      The river she is flowing, down to the sea
      Mother, carry me, a child I will always be
      Mother, carry me, down to the sea

8. **Put money collected in envelope** for landlord or give it to the treasurer.

CHAPTER 6

Maintaining Groups: Guidelines and Group Assessment

The 12 traditions used in 12-step groups provide a value system and a structure that keeps consistency within and between the groups. Whether or not you agree with the content, they have been an important part of the maintenance of the groups. Some form of guidelines are important for maintaining group integrity and binding the group together. Because 16-step groups are based on empowerment, I am not putting out a rigid set of guidelines (other than three *highly recommended* ones). I encourage you to create your own and give you two examples from groups that have worked very well to give you ideas. You will see many commonalities between them.

Recommended Guidelines

The three guidelines listed below are inherent to a 16-step philosophy, which is a wholistic healing program that creates a safe place for people to grow and heal. They are *highly recommended* but are still up to the group to decide.

1. **No smoking during meetings.** *Do not <u>serve</u> caffeinated coffee or tea.* Caffeine is a drug. Avoid eating in groups unless it is being done as part of the group process—an anniversary or celebration. (The group can discuss if it is open to having people bring what they want to drink on an individual basis.)

2. **No seduction or sexual relationships between group members.** This arose from my survey for *Many Roads, One Journey* which indicated the incredible number of seduction stories, inappropriate sexual advances, and sexual abuse that was reported happening in 12-step groups. Groups are like a family and seduction makes the group incestuous. In addition, many people complained that group members assumed a right to touch or hug just because they were in a group together. Because there are so many survivors of sexual abuse in groups and many people with sexually addictive or sexually co-dependent tendencies, it is better to have a clear boundary around sexuality. It is also a matter of respect that everyone should have the right to choose when they are touched or hugged.

On the other hand people may meet and genuinely fall in love in groups. If this happens to you, you should leave the group and join another. This is to keep relationship stress from negatively affecting the group. The tensions of two people struggling in a relationship can often be felt subconsciously or consciously by all participants. Some groups include on-going couples, while others encourage partners to have separate groups. That is up to the group to decide. For more information on this subject, see the chapter on boundaries in *Many Roads, One Journey*.

3. **No therapists/counselors and their current clients in the same group.** Should a therapist/counselor and client find themselves in the same group, it would be appropriate for one of them to leave and find a different group. The person who was there first has priority. Having a therapist/counselor and client in the same group creates a dual relationship and puts the client in a peer position with the counselor. This is inappropriate and against ethics codes for psychologists. It also creates tension for other individuals in the group.

Sample Guidelines

The first set of guidelines comes from a Madison, Wisconsin group that has been very successful. According to the woman who started the group, women are staying sober who were unable to do so in previous groups, and other women are making remarkable strides in their growth. The guidelines are handed out to newcomers and read every few weeks in the group. (There are minor changes from the original). You are welcome to use these guidelines as they are or make changes.

GROUP GUIDELINES
Madison, Wisconsin

1. *Confidentiality.* Anything said, heard, or seen at this group is confidential and needs to be treated as such. Feel free to discuss your experiences with supportive friends, but refrain from discussing the experiences and identities of other group members without their permission. Also, during group, feel free to use only first names or another assumed name.

2. *Outside Contact.* Group members sometimes form outside friendships. This is OK as long as boundaries and limits are agreed on by both people. If group members run into each other outside of group, confidentiality must be remembered and respected. (I would add that it weakens a group to bad mouth/or gossip about anyone in the group or complain about the group. If you have a concern, take it to the meeting for discussion. If you feel critical of others, either work it out with them or shift your focus to your own concerns.)

3. *Touching.* In group it may seem like a normal reaction to reach out and give someone a hug or hold their hand. Touching is allowed only after asking and receiving permission from the person to be touched.

4. *Attendance.* For group consistency and cohesion it is important that members make a commitment to attend regularly. It is important for members to arrive on time and end on time.

5. *Substance Use/Abuse.* Please abstain from alcohol or non-prescription drug use prior to the group. There will be no smoking permitted during group. Because of sensitivity to perfumes, please don't wear scented colognes or perfumes out of respect for those who may have allergies. Also, some women have issues with food, so please do not bring food to group unless you have a medical problem. Non-alcoholic beverages are okay.

6. *Responsibility.* Everyone is responsible for their own feelings, needs, and wants. This means asking for what you need and want from the group and learning to voice your feelings and wants.

7. *Feelings.* All feelings are okay to express.

8. *Respect.* Each of us comes from different and unique experiences and places. We all have different views, opinions, and lifestyles. It is hoped these differences will help us learn and grow. We need to respect and be non-judgmental. We may not agree with each other, but we need to respect each other for who we are right now.

9. *Group Focus.* This is a recovery group for women who are dependent on substances or other people. Please try to stay focused on recovery and solutions to these issues while you are here. Our main focus is using the 16 steps.

10. *Format.* We will take turns talking as one feels moved to speak. There is no cross talking while another is speaking. When one is through speaking she will either say "I want feedback," or express that she does not want feedback. When giving feedback please refrain from giving "You" statements. Rather, make statements like, "I wonder if you are feeling sad. I hear sadness in your voice." or, "It sounds like you did a good job of taking care of yourself!" Try not to make judgments about a person's situation that can lead to feelings of shame or guilt. An example: "I don't think you are doing the right thing..." Before a person gives feedback, check in with the person who just spoke to see if she wants feedback from you. ("Do you want *my* feedback?") This gives the person the choice and is a good exercise in boundary setting.

11. *Sexual Contact.* There will be no sexual touching or sexual contact between group members. Romantic involvement between members of the group interferes with a truly non-judgmental and supportive environment. We ask all members to refrain from romantic contact. If two people do become romantically involved, one person will be expected to drop out of the group.

12. *Closing.* At the end of each group the facilitator will ask for a volunteer to facilitate the next group. The facilitator's role is: to start and end the meeting on time, choose or ask group members to help choose a step to work on during group, announce when it is 15 minutes before the end of the group, and suggest or bring a closing.

SUGGESTED GROUP GUIDELINES
from Chico, California

START ON TIME. END ON TIME

THERE ARE NO 'RIGHT' OR 'WRONG' ANSWERS

EVERYONE HAS THE RIGHT TO PASS

CONFIDENTIALITY: People may talk about what they are learning in the group, but not about other people. The level of trust in the group depends upon it.

"I" STATEMENTS ARE BEST. When revealing your personal experiences, beliefs, and feelings.

MAKE A COMMITMENT IF YOU CAN. The group is open each week to new members: while we realize there will be people who cannot come every time, we ask that people consider making a six, but preferably 16 week commitment.

NO CROSS TALK. Listen and learn from the thoughts, feelings and experiences of group members. Before and after the meeting, participants may share with one another.

FEEDBACK OPTIONAL. At the end of an individual's sharing, if s/he so wishes, persons can ask for feedback, i.e., a reflection from other group members of what they have heard.

AVOID ADVICE GIVING. This is a non-confrontational meeting, unless a person specifically requests it, suggestions, direction, and confrontation should be avoided

T.C.O.Y. (TAKE CARE OF YOURSELF) If the room needs more air, light, heat, etc. please say so and please make it comfortable for everyone.

Exploring the Meaning of Group Guidelines

In putting together this guidebook, I have been constantly walking the line between giving guidance to help people get started, and wanting people to be empowered by finding their own way. On one hand, it is important to learn from the experience of others and not constantly "re-invent the wheel." On the other hand we don't want to be *limited* by the experiences of others, we want to be creative. In general, the more people have a voice in the creation of their group, the more they will be invested in the group.

Sometimes people will simply want to choose a set of guidelines and get started, then decide later if they want to make changes. Other groups might want to experiment with the process described here, as suggested by Aikya Param, an educator, writer and member of a 16-step group. This could be done in one of the early meetings, or it could be done as part of a meeting at a later date.

The following is an adaptation of a letter Aikya wrote concerning the importance of a process that is empowering when we decide on group guidelines. Thank you, Aikya Param, for your contribution.

In a hierarchal, patriarchal system, how things work is established by rules made and imposed by a power-holder and enforced by a certain group among the less powerful. For the individual this usually means that methods and values are imposed from outside by others. The individual is passive and only participates by obedience or disobedience. Since the values and methods come from outside, two problems arise. One is an inner psychological split between the ideal presented by the rulemaker and the actual person and how he or she feels. The other is that the values may not be internalized to become one's values but will simply be behaviors exhibited while the rulemaker or enforcers are present.

Thus the hierarchal method presents problems. Passivity is not a powerful stance. The real person falls short of any ideal at some time or other, sometimes rather often. Thus living with an ideal/actual split inside is the recipe for low self-esteem. Of course, the hierarchal model has benefits or it would not be so popular. In the short term it is an efficient way to get something done and works well in war time, when there's a fire or in other emergencies. Perhaps reliance on it allows us to let all life situations deteriorate until they are emergencies and we can call in a hierarchical emergency team to fix them. In 16-step groups we are not at war or on fire. We are healing and there needs to be another approach.

The ancient Greek teacher Socrates provides a beautiful model of a leader who is not authoritarian. In Socrates' teaching told to us by his disciple Plato, in The Dialogues, *Socrates teaches by asking questions. He almost never tells his students what he wants them to learn. Rather he asks them questions and helps them teach themselves. Basic to this methodology is a firm belief that each person is already wise. This method asks people to bring forth their own wisdom and apply it rather than being told what is right. When people arrive at ideas from inside, as opposed to being handed rules, they have the experience of creating the idea themselves.*

Here is a way groups could have a discussion about the meaning and purpose of guidelines

1. Decide what *subjects* you want included in the guidelines. It could be about anonymity, confidentiality, feedback, cross talk, etc.

2. Instead of reading someone's guideline about confidentiality, the facilitator would say,

> — What do we mean by confidentiality?
> — Why is confidentiality important to us?
> — Could someone give an example of what it means to them personally?
> — Would someone give an example of breaking confidentiality?

3. Have a few people speak and then have the facilitator summarize what has been said.

4. The facilitator could then ask, "Would someone put the guideline into words for us?"

The same process could be applied to the following subjects (plus any others you might think of).

Feedback and cross talk

1. What do we mean by feedback?
2. What do we mean by cross talk?
3. What are basic elements of helpful feedback?
4. How do feedback and cross talk differ?
5. Ask people to give examples of helpful feedback.
6. What are the basic elements of feedback that are not harmful or hurtful?
7. Ask people to give examples of feedback that was not helpful or was harmful.
8. What are some ways people could take charge of getting the feedback they want?

Our role in helping empower others

1. What are ways to talk to people that validate their intelligence and wisdom? People could give personal examples of what is helpful to them.
2. What are ways we can show others we cheer for their strengths and power? People could give examples.
3. What are conflicts you sometimes feel in giving feedback. Am I giving advice or telling my story?

4. When am I feeling judgmental and disguising my judgments with stories or comments? People could share examples of when someone made a "helpful" remark that felt like a disguised judgment.

Authors note: I was impressed by these suggestions and used them in several groups I facilitate. Groups members voiced strong appreciation for the sense of safety this process created. It gave them a safe place to say clearly the kind of feedback they wanted and did not want, thus giving members a sense of control. It also turned out that some people were afraid to appear stupid by asking what "cross talk" and other words meant, and were relieved to have them explained. This is respectful to new members who may not have prior group experience, and do not know group jargon.

Consensus Decisions

The guidelines can be written up following discussion. The group could read them over and see which ones are agreeable for everyone. They could take the ones where people have different thoughts and re-work them until people are comfortable with them. If there is still disagreement on some, the decision could be tabled until the next meeting. The group could then use a consensus process to discuss them and decide on wording. Again, budget your time and don't get lost discussing one particular detail.

Understanding consensus

This section is an adaptation of a pamphlet on consensus put out by The Society of Friends. Consensus is core to empowerment. Consensus does not mean that everyone totally agrees. The idea is that you are working toward group unity yet respecting that people have differences. The most important thing is that all people be heard, and that no one try to change another person. If you do not like a guideline, but think you can live with it and see that the rest of the group is reaching consensus, then you can say, "I agree to step aside in the interest of group unity."

The first step in consensus process is to go around the circle and let each person share their feelings and beliefs without anyone contradicting them as they speak. The mindset is to believe that everyone has a piece of the truth and to listen as if you were in their shoes.

When the group is trying to decide on a guideline (or anything else)
Ask yourself:
— Am I in agreement?
— Am I in partial disagreement, but it is better to take this action than to take none?
— Am I in such disagreement that I must record my disagreement and then stand aside to let the decision stand?
— Am I in such complete disagreement that I must block consensus?

In this model, presumably the last position would not be a surprise to the group, for a person holding this view should have been an active participant in the discussion, trying to discover ways to modify and improve proposed solutions.

Group Assessment/Reflection/Inventory/Check-In

A group assessment creates a safe way for everyone to voice their feelings about the group process. While some people feel comfortable bringing up concerns on their own, it may be scary for others to do so without this invitation. This process can be a time to celebrate how well the group is going as well as voice concerns. It is crucial for any group to take time for reflection and evaluation where everyone's voice is heard. (It's what was missing in many dysfunctional families!) Your group could choose a name for this process such as group reflection, group evaluation or group assessment, inventory or check-up.

An alternative to the steps listed below (which you are welcome to change) is to do a group check in by going through your list of guidelines and see if you are being true to them.

Possible scheduling of group assessment

1. After a set interval (e.g., after every cycle of the 16 steps or every 8 weeks, etc.).
2. At each meeting a few minutes before the group closes, people could voice both their appreciations and concerns.
3. Once a month at the beginning of meeting.
4. Whenever a member calls for a group evaluation. They might bring up one or two particular concerns to be discussed.
5. Have a group assessment frequently in the early stages of the meeting or when it seems that the group is needing it.

When you go through the steps, take time to listen to each person and do not contradict them. You might want to use a talking stick, which means that the person holding the stick is the only one to speak.

Sample group assessment

1. Do we welcome newcomers and help them understand how the group works?
2. Do we cheer for people growing, taking risks, and taking care of themselves (in other words are we bonding through our power, wisdom and strength)?
3. Are we keeping the sharing at a personal level and talking about ourselves (not "what s/he did to me")?
4. Are we sticking to our guidelines about feedback and cross talk?
5. Are we taking good care of ourselves—saying what we need and how we feel?
6. Do we listen to other people with an open mind and if we feel judgmental refrain from giving feedback?
7. Are we keeping the group on track and not letting ourselves be drawn into people's chaos and crises?
8. Do we listen to people's feelings and not try to fix them, rather just let them be where they are on their journey?

9. Are we avoiding advice giving, pat statements and rationalizations? (If you tend to give advice, make pat statements or rationalize people's behavior, you might explore your underlying discomfort with what is being said. Usually the motivation for making fix-it remarks is a fear of feelings, a need to keep distance, or associating shame with strong feelings.)

10. Are we remembering not to monopolize the time?

11. Are we taking enough time for ourselves?

12. Are we respecting people's right to choose when they are touched or hugged.

13. Are we keeping the group free from seduction?

14. Are we refraining from negative talk about anyone in the group when outside of group?

15. Are we starting on time and ending on time? (If we decide to take more time are we making a clear contract to do so?)

16. Take a few minutes to say all the things you appreciate about the group.

Author's note: While it takes some time to agree on format and set guidelines, it is fundamental to empowerment because the group is molded out of the people who attend. Thus, instead of relying on external authority, people generate the structure from their own experience and wisdom. Hopefully this attention to detail will help your group run smoothly. For some groups it might be as simple as picking out a sample set of guidelines and a format, agreeing to use them for a while and getting started. Other people may want to spend more time processing the format and guidelines. No matter what you do, I send best wishes and would like to know how it is going for you.

PART 2

THE 16 STEPS

Readings and Exercises

CHAPTER 7

The Sixteen Steps

The 16 steps were conceived to help people grow, expand and access their wisdom, feelings and power. The belief is that when we fill our lives with connection, joy, purpose and love, the pull of addiction will lose its power. The bottom line is a profound belief in the transforming power of love. Many addictions start in an attempt to feel powerful, filled up and loved. Thus healing means we need to find love, fulfillment and power in self-affirming rather than addictive or self-destructive ways.

Some of the material in this section is drawn from *Many Roads, One Journey.* Other parts are new or have been rewritten. The quotes preceding each step come from questionnaires I sent to existing groups. The exercises/rituals at the end of each step are new. Many of them were contributed by Pat Hanson. I also include an introductory reading you can use at the beginning of meetings that is inclusive of all people. It evolved as I travelled around the country listening to Native Americans, rural Appalachian women, feminists, African Americans, incarcerated women, members of an ashram, working class groups, privileged white males, middle-class women, lesbians and gay men tell their stories. If there is anything I learned a thousand times, it is that people develop addictions for many reasons, and they heal from addiction in countless ways.

As my heart was filled with the richness of these stories, I imagined many groups of diverse people gathering together, sitting in circles telling their stories. This image led me to write an introduction for group meetings that affirms all people's ways. I call it "Many Roads, One Journey: We Gather Together."

As with everything in this book, these steps are offered for your use. *Takes these steps, use them, change them, and then let us know what works for you, so we can pass on the knowledge!*

Many Roads, One Journey
We Gather Together

Our purpose in coming together is to support and encourage each other in moving beyond addiction, dependency and internalized oppression. The only requirement for membership is a desire to maintain sobriety as we each define it.

We come together from many backgrounds and we can learn from each other's ways and experiences. Yet, none of us has the answers for another person. We do not impose our beliefs on others or expect others to tell us the way. We have faith that through determination, sharing our histories of discovery and healing, supporting each other, and understanding the impact of our social system on us, we can each discover our personal path toward healing and sobriety.

Growing and becoming strong is a balance between self acceptance and a firm commitment to sobriety. We overcome addiction and internalized oppression because we want to honor and enjoy the life we have been given and be of service to others. This process is not about moral worth. We are all sacred children of Creation this moment.

These steps for discovery and empowerment are designed to create a healthy, aware Self which, over time, will crowd out compulsive, addictive or dependent behavior. We believe that through bonding with others, speaking genuinely from our hearts, forgiving ourselves and others, finding purpose, helping create social change, and accepting the imperfections of life, we will find a sense of fulfillment that we have sought to fill through our addictive and dependent behavior.

The journey is sometimes difficult, sometimes smooth. This is natural. As we let go of our addictions and empower ourselves, some of us may use other resources to help us grow. We may also be faced with difficult circumstances in our lives that need advocacy and assistance. We support each other as we explore all avenues of personal empowerment and growth.

Several things you may want to remember as you use these steps:

- There is no perfect path, only the path you choose one day at a time.

- While we are aware of the powerful nature of addiction, we have seen our collective will and commitment to sobriety and growth is even more powerful.

- Change takes time and is made of many small steps.

- Many people have moved beyond addiction and internalized oppression.

- The steps are only suggestions; change them in any way you like so they feel true to your heart.

Charlotte Kasl, *Many Roads, One Journey*. © 1991, Sixteen Steps for Dis-covery and Empowerment

16 Steps for Discovery and Empowerment

Through the Voices of Many Women and Men

1) We affirm we have the power to take charge of our lives and stop being dependent on substances or other people for our self-esteem and security.

   Alternative: We admit/acknowledge we are out of control with/powerless over _____ yet have the power to take charge of our lives and stop being dependent on substances or other people for our self-esteem and security.

2) We come to believe that God/Goddess/Universe/Great Spirit/Higher Power awakens the healing wisdom within us when we open ourselves to that power.

3) We make a decision to become our authentic selves and trust in the healing power of the truth.

4) We examine our beliefs, addictions, and dependent behavior in the context of living in a hierarchical, patriarchal culture.

5) We share with another person and the Universe all those things inside of us for which we feel shame and guilt.

6) We affirm and enjoy our intelligence, strengths and creativity, remembering not to hide these qualities from ourselves and others.

7) We become willing to let go of shame, guilt and any behavior that keeps us from loving ourselves and others.

8) We make a list of people we have harmed and people who have harmed us, and take steps to clear out negative energy by making amends and sharing our grievances in a respectful way.

9) We express love and gratitude to others and increasingly appreciate the wonder of life and the blessings we do have.

10) We learn to trust our reality and daily affirm that we see what we see, we know what we know and we feel what we feel.

11) We promptly admit to mistakes and make amends when appropriate, but we do not say we are sorry for things we have not done, and we do not cover up, analyze or take responsibility for the shortcomings of others.

12) We seek out situations, jobs, and people that affirm our intelligence, perceptions and self-worth and avoid situations or people who are hurtful harmful, or demeaning to us.

13) We take steps to heal our physical bodies, organize our lives, reduce stress and have fun.

14) We seek to find our inward calling, and develop the will and wisdom to follow it.

15) We accept the ups and downs of life as natural events that can be used as lessons for our growth.

16) We grow in awareness that we are sacred beings, interrelated with all living things, and we contribute to restoring peace and balance on the planet.

STEP 1

We affirm we have the power to take charge of our lives and stop being dependent on substances or other people for our self-esteem and security.

"Just acknowledging this step as the truth is helping me get a grip on my inner strength."

"After going through treatment 9 times and failing to stay sober I started believing that I actually was powerless. I needed something to tell me I could do it—not that I couldn't. I made it 10 months going to a 16-step meeting, relapsed over some incest memories, went back to 16-step meetings and I'm back to 7 months. When I tell AA people I don't think I'm powerless I get a lot of raised eyebrows and 'looks,' but ...*I'll never say I'm powerless again.*"

"I felt powerless and victimized. By saying this first step and thinking about it I began to notice the choices I have."

"I finally became ashamed of clinging to my smoking habit while reading this step every week. I quit."

We start our journey toward healing with an affirmation of our inner strength instead of referring to substances or other people: within us lies the ability to overcome addiction/dependency and take charge of our lives. This includes overcoming psychological and economic dependencies on others as well. For women and oppressed peoples, to affirm our power is to confront one of the deepest parts of our internalized oppression—namely, that we are inferior to and dependent on other people or authority figures for our self-esteem and security. We may not feel we have the power to take charge of our lives, but as we start affirming the possibility and bond with others, our power grows. This step does not deny the power of the addiction, it simply affirms our inner strength—a fundamental resource for overcoming addiction or other problems.

The wording of this first step is particularly relevant for people who experience depression or are in dependent relationships. In both cases the underlying problem is often a feeling of helplessness or a lack of self (although severe mental problems may have an organic component). Because addictions are adopted to create a false sense of security and self-esteem, this step suggests we ask: What truly brings me a sense of self-esteem and security? How have I used drugs, alcohol, possessions, gangs, fancy homes, status, TV, romance, money or sex to create the *illusion* of self-esteem and security? How have I as an individual taken on another person's definition of what I should be? How has my community or ethnic group taken on the values of another culture or group of people?

Once we acknowledge the addiction and commit ourselves to sobriety we can shift our focus, look at our values and think of what *truly* brings self-esteem and security.

It's as if we take our self-esteem, draw it into ourselves, and connect it to our inner world instead of having it tied to a string of outside sources. Central to our journey is repeatedly asking ourselves: What am I doing that is true to my spirit, my heritage and my heart? What am I doing to bring purpose and meaning into my life? What am I doing to take care of myself?

The phrase "stop being dependent on substances or other people for our self-esteem or security" asks that we name our dependencies and addictions. We need to say, I am addicted to this substance, to compulsive eating, to this person, to sex, to drugs, whatever. Then we need to assess the harm of our addiction: What has it cost us emotionally, physically, spiritually? We need to link the harmful consequences to the addiction so we start realizing the cost of our addiction. This is like sending a shock wave to the survival brain. Listen up! We're in trouble here. We need to do something. This is serious.

Linking the addiction to the harmful consequences can be an ongoing process. At first people may see addictions and emotional problems as isolated problems. With a first step, you think of *all* the ways your addiction or behavior has affected you and the people around you. Often the consequences of the addiction are far broader than you ever imagined and you only realized the breadth of consequences after giving up the addiction and staying tuned in to your emotions and behavior over a long period of time.

Alternative: *We admit we were out of control with/powerless over _____, yet have the power to take charge of our lives and stop being dependent on substances or other people for our self-esteem and security.*

In submitting these steps to people for feedback, many liked the first version and others felt strongly that they needed to start the first step by saying, "I am *powerless* over_____ (my addiction or the person I'm wanting to change)." The idea is that you gain power by acknowledging the things you are powerless to control. Saying "I am *powerless* over... a substance or a person" sets off an alarm inside. "I've lost control. This behavior/addiction is dangerous. I need help. I can't handle this stuff. No way! Never! It's wrecking my life. It's hurting my health. It's destroying my peace of mind.

People also said it was crucial to say, "I am powerless over...(another person)." It's crucial to realize the futility of controlling others. It reminds us that we can't change another person...but we can change ourselves. When your life has been under siege from an addiction or dependency you need a sharp, clear, stinging reminder that you have lost control and that your addiction is messing up your life.

A way to modify the use of the term powerless is to use it as an adverb. Instead of "I'm powerless over_____," you could say, "I *feel* powerless, or "I *experience* myself as powerless." It's important to sort out that we may *feel* powerless over our impulses, cravings or desires, but ultimately we are *not* powerless. We have the power to make choices. We can have the *urge* to drink and *choose* not to. We can *want* to binge and *choose* to take a walk instead. We can *want* to seduce a certain man or woman, and *choose* not to. We can *want* to go on a shopping spree and *choose* to stay home, or call a friend.

❖ ◆ ❖ ◆ ❖

Suggested Exercises for Step 1:

1. *Link the addiction to the harmful consequences—taking a 1st step*
   Taking a first step traditionally means writing down one's addiction history and sharing it with another person or a group. *The point is to connect the addiction to the harmful consequences.* The consequences can be external and internal—smashed up cars, loss of jobs, outbursts of anger, violent behavior, getting arrested, and they can be ulcers, tension, liver problems, depression and emotional deadness. It's a practice in many groups to have a person tell the story of their addiction—when it started, what form it took, and the damage it caused. It can be very emotional to read a first step to a group because it opens up the feelings of loss and harm due to one's addiction/dependency. (It is important, however, as soon as possible to move forward to a plan for living and not dwell on past addictive behavior.)

2. *Know the cues to your addiction*
   a) List all the situations and cues that tend to trigger your addiction or self-defeating behavior. It can be going to bars, going to a bakery, certain movies, wearing certain clothes, talking in an affected way, obsessive fantasizing, being with certain people and on and on. This is your survival list. Share it with the group and read it on a daily basis.

   b) List all the permission giving statements you have used to allow yourself to act out your addiction. (Just one more time. I really need this. This won't really matter. I can always stop tomorrow.) Share them with the group.

3. *Link the addiction to the positive intention*
   a) Talk about the positive intention underlying your addictive or dependent behavior? Were you covering over pain from abuse? Were you trying to fit in with a group of people? Were you trying to fill an emptiness inside? Was your life bleak, and the addiction made you feel happy?

   b) Now think of ways you could fulfill your positive intention without harming yourself. For example, I can *fill this emptiness* by talking with others and with prayer and meditation. I can *fit in* by joining a group of people who are getting healthy. I can learn to *release this pain* from abuse by talking about it. I can *have a richer life* by learning a vocation. You can also state these affirmations in the present tense: I *am* filling this emptiness by talking with others and so on.

4. *Affirming you have choices/power*

a) Past choices. Go around the circle with each person stating a choice they made in the last week to take care of him or herself. Examples: I have chosen not to drink all week. I have chosen not to watch more than one hour a day of TV all week. I have chosen to write down affirmations. I have chosen to exercise. I have chosen to eat vegetables every day.

b) Future choices. Go around the circle and have each person affirm their ability to make choices. You can use the phrase "I choose to…" or "I have the power…" or "I can learn to…" "I choose to stay sober." "I can learn to speak up for myself." "I choose to hang up the phone when someone gets abusive." "I choose to call friends." "I choose to talk about my feelings." If you like, you can have people cheer each other on by saying, "Yes! You can! Right! Go!" or some other response after people state the choices they can make. This helps get the message get reinforced in the brain.

5. *Sharing our strengths*

a) Have each person go around the circle and tell of times throughout their life that they took a risk in their best interest. Brave acts can include crying in front of someone, asking for help, taking charge of a situation, standing up to someone, telling secrets, admitting to fear, saying no, saying yes. Whatever affirms your truths and helps you grow. Be sure to remember times from your childhood.

b) Variation: The Ante up game. To keep people from rationalizing, minimizing, or qualifying what they say, give everyone five matches or toothpicks. Whenever you qualify or belittle yourself you have to ante up a match. If someone is wonderful, you can give them a match. (This can be a lot of fun and you can apply it to other exercises!)

6. *Experience the effect of language. I am powerless vs. I feel powerless vs. I have the power*

a) Have group members write down as quickly as possible a list of all the things they have felt powerless over/dependent upon. List everything that comes to mind: television, jobs, drugs, alcohol, rage, violence, sex, stealing, cigarettes, shopping, or a specific relationship.

b) Pair up. Take an item that relates to you and put it in the following sentences. Then repeat the statements two or three times to your partner listening internally to how you feel:

> "I *am* powerless over _____."
> "I *feel* powerless over _____ yet I have the power to change."
> "I *experience* myself as powerless over_____ yet I have the power to change."
> "I *have* the power to stop (using) _____ and to take charge of my life."

Talk about any differences you felt between these statements. Tell how your body felt and if your energy level, clarity, or sense of hope changed.

7. *A Self-esteem circle*

This is a great way to start groups on a weekly basis.

a) Quickly go around the room and have everyone congratulate themselves for anything new or good they did during the week. Have others cheer, applaud, or say *good for you*. For example, "I told Beth how much I appreciated her." *Yay! Good for you!!* "I asked a friend over to teach me how to cook brown rice and veggies." "I told my mother I had to get off the phone." *Yes, Yes! That's great.* The person who is "it" could tell the others what he or she wants to hear. "I want you to say I was brave and courageous," or "I want you to say I was caring and considerate."

STEP 2

We come to believe that God/Goddess/Universe/Great Spirit/Higher Power awakens the healing wisdom within us when we open ourselves to that power.

"I love this step. For years I've believed in inner wisdom and have...needed to learn to trust it, as this step reminds me to do."

"Talking about my spiritual journey brings it into my daytime waking consciousness. Then it can be part of my day's transactions."

"This step has helped my spirituality flow through me and connect to the power in the Universe. There is no beginning or end, no inside me or outside me—just a powerful force that exists everywhere."

"It is fascinating in group to hear people tell of their spiritual journeys. Even though they all sound different on the outside, underneath I realize how much we all seem to be seeking the same thing."

The important elements in this step are hope, faith and developing strength.

When we're about to give up an addiction or dependency, it sometimes feels as if we're sitting at the edge of a cliff, being urged to jump. It seems impossible to imagine how we could live without the addiction—that protective shield that felt like a best friend—and return to life with all its pain and struggle. A way to help us take the leap is with the belief that there's something better, another way, and we can find it. It helps to realize we don't have to do it alone because there exists a power bigger than the addiction that will replace the addiction. Ultimately that power is love and will.

By stating our willingness to tap the power of the Universe and draw it into us, we ignite our will, which gives us courage and strength for the journey. It is an active union between ourselves and the power of the Universe. If you don't relate to the term spirituality or the concept of God, Goddess or Great Spirit, then substitute the words love, or truth: I come to believe that love will awaken the healing wisdom within me when I open myself to its power, or I come to believe that living by my truths will awaken the healing power within me.

Our minds can be a tremendous ally to help ignite our will. Every positive thought creates change in our cells, brain and heart. Another way to tap into the power of the Universe is by simply taking a deep breath, relaxing, going inside and calling out from within: Help, Give me courage, Give me strength, I am willing to be well. We can also find power through prayer, meditation, affirmations, exercise, being with positive people, going to talks and workshops, and simply opening our senses to all the beauty that is around us because God/the Goddess, or the Great Spirit is everywhere, in all living things. It's not just "out there." It is as close as breath itself.

I want to underscore the incredible power that comes through *authentic* contact with other people. Repeatedly making genuine human contact starts giving us a sense of being filled up and a knowledge of love. Many people who become addicted were never securely attached to a parent or caregiver, and they have gone through their whole lives feeling starved for connection. A loving, secure attachment to a parent helps a child develop the ability to access the power of the Universe, although deprivation is sometimes the catalyst for the search as well. Thus being with people who affirm us and are honest with us can fill a developmental step that is often missing. Sometimes being with people will feel good, and then we are immediately lonely when we are again alone. This is part of the process and with time, you will carry with yourself the sense of connection you felt with others and no longer feel so lonely on your own. Other sources of spirit come through being in nature and taking on new challenges.

Exercises for Step 2:

1. ***Define your spirituality or sources of faith and strength***
   Go around the circle and talk about your concept of spirituality—not just as an abstract concept, but how it works on a day-to-day basis. Give specific examples from situations in your life. If the term spirituality doesn't connect for you, or seems too personal to talk about, talk about experiences that have given you hope, kind things people have done for you, and other sources of strength in your life.

2. ***Knowing your own truth***
   Remember a time when you had a gut feeling, an intuitive sense of something, or a decision that came clear for you—you *knew* what you needed to do, or you became clear about a decision you had been mulling over. Describe the situation in detail and say how you felt.

3. ***Opening ourselves up to the power of the Universe"***
   Circle around the group talking about ways you make room for your inner wisdom to come alive: Taking quiet time to breathe? Affirmations? Meditation? Reading? Hiking? Praying? Sports? Writing? Listening to your dreams?

   Then take one or two of these methods and try them out for a week or more. Then in subsequent weeks try out other methods. Be sure and try something long enough to see if it helps. Over the next weeks, come back to group and talk about your experiences. Which way helped the most? In what ways did it help you? Which were difficult? Which raised your fear level? Which were easy?

4. Take a class or buy a book that emphasizes conscious breathing. It can be meditation, yoga or Kundalini breathing. If this is not possible, try walking on a regular basis keeping your awareness on your breathing. The point is to open up the flow of energy inside you and connect it to the Wisdom of the Universe.

STEP 3

We make a decision to become our authentic selves and trust in the healing power of the truth.

"My FAVORITE! This one has been like a banner, a continuous motto for me."

"I just love the word "authentic." This step reminds me to stop and really feel out what I am doing, saying and thinking. Is it what I *really* mean?"

"For years I denied my sexuality, my intuition and my ignorance (I had to be all intelligent—my version of perfect). I shut down my body and fought with its natural shape. This step gave me the energy to release the false and accept the reality of me. By saying the words out loud, 'I'm sexual, I love to dance, I don't want to edit my language,' I got the courage to really listen to myself deeply and act on what I heard. Other members of the group encouraged me by sharing their similar experiences and listening to their own inner voices."

"The authentic self operating in the world was unknown to me. I was a collection of fragments and roles when I started attending 16-step meetings. Then I gave myself permission to make choices, try doing things differently... Now I feel there is an authentic self who has emerged and is not composed of fragments."

"I work diligently on this step daily. It helped me be able to admit out loud what I did and didn't believe in...It started me on my search inward."

"As a one parent family with roots in Mexico and Spanish spoken in the home, I learned to see the great strength we give each other in being who we are."

In our attempts to survive in our family or culture, we learned to dance between our real self and a false or adaptive self. We learned to please, be wild, sexy, sweet, cool, charming, tough—whatever it took to get attention, care or help us feel safe. This was the best we could do at the time. Yet to become empowered, we need to gently drop the facade and become our natural selves. We need to be an authentic person no matter what situation we are in. We need to be truthful and honest.

Knowledge of God/Goddess/Spirit begins with knowledge of self. If we are to be one with the spirit, we must know ourselves. This means allowing ourselves to meet our inner world of thoughts, feelings, and sometimes buried memories. It means we stop taking directions from others, stop faking the smiles, the bravado, the innocence, the power, the charm, the docility, the orgasm, and that we continue to reach deep inside, asking ourselves, what is *my* truth?

For some, the false front has taken over so completely there is little memory of an authentic person, so the task will be to build a self through constantly going inside and asking: What do I think, what do I believe, what is good for me, what do I want? (In *Women, Sex and Addiction* there is a chapter called "Codependent Sobriety" that gives many suggestions for building a self.)

We could re-word "We make a *decision to*" to "We become *willing* to...." We are *willing* to be uncomfortable in order to grow. We are *willing* to make scary changes. We are *willing* to feel. We are *willing* to be happy. Many people say they *want* to get well, but when it comes to actually doing something hard, they pull back. A way to check this out for yourself is to take a deep breath, go inside and say with all your being, *I'm willing to do whatever it takes to heal/be whole.* Then listen to the response. *But not....*work fewer hours. *But not...*give up this crummy relationship. *But not...*get a steady job. *But not...*live with less money. *But not...* take time everyday to meditate, exercise or say affirmations. *But not...* face my childhood abuse, and so on and so on. The rush of fear that hits people when they say "I am willing to do whatever it takes" is the old survivor or addictive side shrieking with terror at the idea of change. Don't shame that part of you. Rather, like a wise and loving parent talk to your fears: What's going on? Are you scared? You can handle it. I can help you. We don't need to panic. I'll be with you and take care of you.

Finding our truths often means sorting out our addictive impulses from actions that would be in our best interest. Sometimes we listen inwardly and hear nothing. Sometimes the voices collide inside, and we feel stuck in confusion. One moment we feel sure we have the best solution, and a few moments later we're not so sure. Just as we are about to take a positive step for ourselves, the addictive (frightened) part mounts a counterattack. Confusion is a natural part of the process, but keep listening. It takes time to find and trust the voices within. People often develop phrases to help them reach for the truth. They ask: What does my wise woman/man say? What does my highest self say? What do I really believe? Which way would be loving of myself?

The second part of this step *'and trust in the healing power of truth'* is one of the most important aspects of spiritual growth. Living by our truths is like living aligned with our deepest wisdom. A guiding principle is that acting on spiritual truths will never bring harm to ourself or others. For example, instead of trying to manipulate a situation, we reach for the words that speak from our heart. This often involves a willingness to let go of the outcome. For example, instead of trying to control a relationship by acting the "right" way, you attempt to be honest and see if there is a fit in the relationship. Approached this way, relationships are not devastating if they don't work out.

As we start to trust in the truth, we speak the words that have stuck in our throats. We bring up conflict. We say what we want, believe and feel. We say "no," we say "yes." We apologize, express gratitude or ask for help. This doesn't mean that we don't occasionally compromise or go along with others, but we don't fake it or pretend to be a certain way to control others. Sometimes it takes a while to learn that the truth doesn't always harm people or drive them away. It can help tremendously to remember, *No matter what you say or do, some people will like you and some people won't.* So you might as well be your truest self, because you'll feel better and create more intimate relationships. You may lose some friends or partners who liked you better when you faked it or acted out a role, but in the long run you will attract people who also want to live by their truths...and that can be very sweet and affirming.

Exercises for Step 3:

1. Willingness and readiness

    a) Divide a piece of paper down the middle. On the left hand side write, *What I need to do to be free.* On the right hand side write, *What will make it happen*, or *what will it take.* Be specific. Examples: Tell your mother you'd like her to make some of the long distance calls. Limit the conversation with a friend who is in constant crisis and drains your energy. Tell your father you don't want to hear sexist jokes. Ask for a raise. Set a limit with a child. Stop taking so much work home from the office. Stop making all the coffee at work. Take a dance class. Speak up in a class. Call someone to get together. Then go down the other side of the paper and write in what would help make it happen. For example. You decide you are going to tell a friend you don't want to listen to constant negative talk. In the "What will make it happen" column, you could write. Talk about it with a support person who is good at setting limits. Role play doing it. Write out your script. After you've done it, celebrate by having lunch with your support person. If you don't succeed, try, try again.

    To do this in pairs:
    Person one says:
    "What do you need to do to be free?"
    Following the answer, ask,
    "What will make it happen?" Do this over and over.

    b) Say to yourself or to a partner ...

      "I am willing to do whatever it takes to heal/be whole."
      Then write down everything that comes up. "But not_____."
      Discuss the experience and the feelings.

2. Recreating yourself

This is best done with a partner, but one can take the essence of this exercise into everyday life. When you speak to each other take time to breathe and put energy into your words. Visualize the new behavior actually happening. Generate as much energy flow as you can. You can substitute the word "see" for "create."

      Person 1 asks, "How do you want to be?"
      Person 2 answers
      Person 1 says, "I create you as [the way you want to be]."
      Person 2 says "I create myself as..."

An example:

Person 1: "How do you want to be?"

Person 2: "I want to remember to take time to listen to my lover and not always talk about myself."

Person 1: "I create you as being interested in listening to your lover and finding it truly rewarding."

Person 2: "I create myself as being interested in listening to my lover and being able to empathize better."

3.   *"Become our authentic selves"... remember we are more than our labels*

a)   In pairs, sitting face to face, one person asks another the question

"Who are you?" After one reply such as 'a woman,' ask again "Who are you?" Listen for the reply. Without responding ask again, "Who else are you?" After two minutes, change roles.

Discuss all the various identities and the feelings that came up.

b)   *Moving beyond labels.* Take the blank mandala in the back of the book, page 121, and fill it in with all the labes that describe yourself. Let yourself feel all those parts of you. Then share your mandala in the group. After everyone has had a turn, go around the circle and have each person put their mandala in the middle of the room while saying (something to the effect), "I am not my labels. I let go of my labels. I am a spirit, I am life, I am sacred just as I am without these labels." After everyone has done this have a few minutes of silence to take in the experience. You may want to discuss it, or you may want to just take it in silently.

c)   You could also make your own "Who am I" mandala by putting up a big piece of paper somewhere in your house and covering it with clippings, stories, words, pictures, poems that reflect who you are.

d)   As a ritual or celebration have everyone bring a poem, clipping, pictures, stickers, ribbon, magic markers, and make a mandala for one or more people. Say something about what you brought as you put it on the mandala. Then sign your names or write a note and present it. We often do this when a person is leaving a group.

4.   *Trust in the healing power of the truth*

a)   Close your eyes and think of something you have wanted to say recently, but had difficulty expressing. Write down exactly what you want to say without editing it. Be outrageous, let out the stops! Put the pieces of paper in a hat/basket/ pile. Then have people draw them out of "the hat" and read them out loud. Have fun and be dramatic. Once everyone has read their statement, members could volunteer to have the group brainstorm how to say what they need to say in a way that is powerful, respectful and simple.

b) Close your eyes and imagine a troublesome situation or a decision you are trying to make. Then take a few deep breaths and relax and repeatedly say to yourself, The truth is.... (I feel, I want, I need, I don't like, this relationship isn't working, I need a break, etc.) Stay with "the truth is" until you feel something happen inside. You may immediately hear yourself start to argue with the truth because it suggests you need to take an action that is scary. If that happens, simply take note of the arguments.

Share your experience with others in the group.

c) For one week keep a journal noticing times and situations when you are fearful. Try to remind yourself of the causes of fear when you feel scared. See whether there is a *real danger* present or whether your fear is based on old messages in your head. Do this for one week and report what you learned to the group.

STEP 4

We examine our beliefs, addictions, and dependent behavior in the context of living in a hierarchal, patriarchal culture.

"In our group we all became more gentle with ourselves in relation to negative self-talk or struggles with jobs, kids and money, when put against the backdrop of society, rather than as a character defect."

"In AA, I unwittingly absorbed the idea that talking about the oppression in our society was tantamount to being ungrateful and wasting time on things we cannot change. In reality, talking about patriarchy and hierarchy frees me to see that we can find a spirituality that is authentic to ourselves. Something we have in our gut and heart..."

"I began to realize how I oppressed myself and that...I would need to become more comfortable with conscious decision-making."

"In the group, I was angry about the culture, felt hopeless at times, but then a power came through me and I said very loudly 'someone's got to change this shit and it looks like it's up to us to do it.' We are doing it by being in this group!"

In step three we talked about becoming your authentic self. This is a scary thing to do in our society, because the stereotypes assigned to different groups of people encourage them *not* to become their authentic selves, rather to adopt limiting roles. Thus, becoming a whole, powerful, loving, integrated human being is a radical political act because it goes against the status quo of sex-role and racial stereotypes.

Earlier I spoke of internalized oppression. You might want to reread that section when using this step. In healing from addictions and emotional problems, *we need to see how our dysfunctional culture lives in us, and perpetuates addiction and emotional problems.* Then we need to take the negative voices out of our bodies, minds and spirits.

It is not surprising that in the '80s we gave a lot of attention to understanding addiction, abuse and incest in the context of "dysfunctional families." While it has been extremely helpful for people, it's a bit like examining a sick tree by looking at the leaves and not the roots. Families transmit the values of our hierarchal, patriarchal culture, which are the roots of our dysfunctional system. (The dysfunction being measured by the amount of crime, battering, killings, abuse, incest, inequality, poverty, addiction, loneliness, discrimination, depression, stress-related illness and emotional problems, as opposed to economic indicators.) Also, families can work very hard to impart good values and be sabotaged by social norms such as gangs, drugs, violence and poverty.

We receive confusing messages from the culture and then think we are the source of the confusion. For example, if you're a woman you get the message, don't be too smart or you won't attract a man; if you're a man, you're taught not to be gentle, sensitive and thoughtful, or you'll be called a sissy, queer, wimp or girl. That's like saying kill off a part of yourself to be accepted. Have you ever stopped to inventory how much stress you have in your life due to inequities in the system? What are all the adaptations you make on a daily basis walking the line between surviving in patriarchy while trying to be true to yourself? Understanding this is crucial in terms of developing a healthy aware ego and your ability to become wary and wise.

Part of empowerment is to give up being naive and innocent about the exploitation and inequities in our system. We need to know the face of danger, protect ourselves and work toward a more just and compassionate system. We need to know a con when we see it and to recognize when we are being manipulated. This leads us to recognize the cultural source of our problems, so we can affirm our rights instead of slithering into shame, feeling stupid, or venting our anger on our loved ones when we are being oppressed. There are chapters on this subject in *Many Roads, One Journey* and in *Women, Sex, and Addiction.*

Exercises for Step 4:

1. *Demystifying difficult words*
Some people in and out of 16-step groups have more difficulty pronouncing the words *pay-tri-ar-chy* .... and *hi-er-ar-chy* than understanding them. Have a few people pronounce these words in your group. Then have people go around and give their understanding of patriarchy and hierarchy.

2. *Recognizing the voices of oppression*
   a) Have each person make a list of:

      — the thoughts that stop you from being honest, authentic, spontaneous or joyful;

      — the internal voices of despair, fear and hopelessness;

      — the beliefs that get you into trouble, violent situations or dependent relationships;

      — the everyday situations in which you feel fear or apprehension (like being in a parking ramp at night, living in a violent neighborhood, speaking up for yourself at work, or simply saying "no" or "yes" to a friend.) Have people share their lists and then as a group brainstorm the themes that have emerged.

   b) Go through the list of messages and think about how they got in your head. Give specific examples of what parents/teachers/authorities said, what you read, what you got from the media, what happened to you?

   c) Brainstorm all the ways you could talk back to the limiting, self-defeating or negative voices in your head. "I hear you. You're wrong. I can do things differently." My personal favorite is "I *will not* live in fear."

   d) Brainstorm what you could actually do in your life to break through these limitations and become a more secure, productive, powerful, happy person.

NOTE: (A brainstorm is when everyone throws out ideas and no one criticizes or comments. Be as wild and creative as you can.)

3. **Tell your story on hierarchy**
    The drawing of hierarchy/patriarchy on page 116. See also pages 117 and 118 for more exercises related to hierarchy/patriarchy.

    a) Choosing one question from page 117 or 118 could be a short exercise for a group to do together.

    b) Use the questions from pages 117 and 118 as an exercise outside of group. Groups of two or three people could set a time to get together and go through all the questions that accompany the hierarchy chart. Then everyone could report back to the group.

4. **Sex roles, sexuality and addictions**
    Go to page 126 and fill in the worksheet. Then break into small groups and go around the circle sharing one item at a time.

    After you have done this, brainstorm any parallels or similarities to your own addictions/dependencies that you see in our culture: the budget, for example!

5. **Body image and patriarchy/hierarchy**
    As a group, brainstorm all of the ways our culture has impacted your body (stress, substance use, eating disorders, work), your mind (stress, burn-out, depression), and your spirit (apathy, hopelessness, alienation, fear).

6. **Sexuality and patriarchy/hierarchy**
    a) Talk about the ways your sexuality has been defined in the culture—how you "should" have sex, with whom, where, when, who initiates, what is appropriate sexual behavior for you (in terms of gender, class, race ethnicity, religion, etc). Talk in the group about how this has impacted you.

        What has been good for you?
        What has been harmful for you?

    b) As a group discussion, imagine what your sexuality would be like if there were no violence, inequality, incest, abuse, rape, battering or economic deprivation in the world? (Possible questions to ask: How would sex have been explained in your family? What would role models be like? What would the attitude toward same sex relationships be? What would advertisements look like? How would you feel about initiating sex or asking for what you want with a sexual partner? How would you feel emotionally during sex? How would your sexuality be aligned with your spirituality?)

7. **Rent the video Goddess Remembered** and watch it on your own, or with a group of friends. It is put out by the Canadian Film Board. Other suggested videos, *"The Power of One, The Milagro Bean Field Wars* and *Silkwood..*

STEP 5

We share with another person and the Universe all those things inside of us for which we feel shame and guilt.

> "I did this sharing of my shame and guilt with a women I recently met. She said all she heard was loss. This is making me wonder about what *I* consider my shame and guilt."

> "It feels so much kinder to talk about shame and guilt than about shortcomings and defects of character."

> "This step gave me courage to speak about my shame. I may never have done it without this push. The results were excellent and the effect keeps on positively."

No matter what the source of our shame and guilt, it is important to talk about these inner tyrants in order to clear out dense energy in the body. Whatever we deny or keep secret is like toxic energy poisoning our system. It is important that we talk about sexual abuse, loneliness, unskillful or mean things we've done—anything that blocks our ability to love ourselves. By clearing out our secrets, we deflate the power of the shame and guilt. It can be a wonderful relief to find that people listen respectfully and don't keel over with disgust or say, "That's too terrible. Get out of here!" Maybe those terrible things we did don't mean we should be thrown off the planet. Maybe I'm not such a bad and shameful person after all. Because secrets shared become sacred truths, this step helps us love and accept ourselves.

This is an internal cleansing step that is often a long-term process, particularly if we are survivors of incest, battering or abuse. When we talk about shameful things done to us, particularly sexual abuse, we experience the shame it created inside us. Thus we sometimes need to go slowly to prevent being overwhelmed.

The timing of this step is important. It's a dance between not repressing so much that you start wanting to act out, and yet not going so deeply into your pain that you feel overwhelmed. For some people it is better to get their life under control and take care of basic security needs before delving into the painful past. This is also true for people who are depressed: it is usually well advised to have cognitive therapy, focus on the present, take control and get a routine established. One needs ego strength and a safe haven in order to journey into painful territory. Many people spoke of harmful therapy were they were pushed to look at incest and abuse when they were deeply depressed or in the early stages of discovery. If things start happening too fast, tell yourself to slow down this process. Tell your therapist as well!

Sometimes, after two or three years of sobriety, people's pain erupts with great intensity. Many people find they need to take a month out, possibly go to a healing program or hospital so they have a safe place to let go. This is not going backward or regressing as so many people think. It is having enough ego strength and healing to be able to face some of the underlying pain. So don't despair if this happens—it's often part of the process.

Exercises/Discussion for Step 5:

1. *Taking a fifth step*
    Make a list of everything inside that feels shameful or painful. This may take a period of time, so don't feel overwhelmed. Then set a time (often two to four hours) to go through the list with someone you deeply trust. While traditional fifth steps have been done with clergy, many people do this step with peers in their group or trusted friends. Releasing secrets can feel safer when we meet as equal human beings, in the spirit of helping each other heal. (There is a lengthy discussion of fifth steps in *Many Roads, One Journey.*)

2. *A group fifth step*
    A group fifth step is when people collectively clear out their secrets with each other. This can be approached in many ways. People can write down a list in advance and bring it to the group, or they can take some time to breathe, reach inside and listen for whatever comes up as the ritual proceeds. A list can help us remember things, but it's important to share from the heart and not just read through a list in a detached way. Some groups like to light a candle and put a pillow or something symbolic in the center of the room. Sharing our secrets in the confidentiality of our groups bonds us together in trust and helps us love and accept ourselves. People can speak in any order. It can help to have a short meditation in the beginning and then let people speak whenever something comes to mind. No one is to respond.

    Variation: Groups can choose one topic like sexuality. This brings a focus to a difficult subject.

3. *Group writing exercise*
    Take three pieces of paper.

    > On one page write: Things I would tell an acquaintance.
    > On another page write: Things I would tell a good friend.
    > On the third page write: Things I would share with almost no one.

    a) Someone collects and reads aloud the "acquaintance" secrets. After that, people say a few words about what they are feeling.

    b) Someone reads the secrets you would tell a good friend and group members share their reactions. Again, people talk about what they are feeling.

    IMPORTANT: Only if all people in the group agree do you go on to level three secrets. If it feels like too much for anyone, then stop after level two secrets.

c) Someone reads level three secrets and group members share their reactions.

d) A ritual is carried out to let go of the secrets. People could crumple up the papers and burn them or tear up the pieces of paper, and burn them.

e) People could then talk, chant or do a ritual to mark the power and importance of clearing out negative energy.

STEP 6

We affirm and enjoy our intelligence, strengths and creativity, remembering not to hide these qualities from ourselves and others.

"At 35 I had forgotten how many talents I have. I am an athlete, a musician, a good mother, friend and teacher. This step allows me to celebrate and dance in joy and gratitude."

"This one I enjoy so much. We all get happy, smile and laugh a lot. I get to reveal my imagination...so many of us hide and disguise our feelings and thoughts."

"I refer to this step when I...need to concentrate or focus on my art."

"I started a 6th step celebration. That was a meeting when each person would say something good about themselves that they wanted to celebrate. The next part was that each of us would say what we appreciated about the person to our right or left. These celebrations are uncomfortable, loving and wonderfully healing."

(NOTE: This step has been changed since the publication of *Many Roads, One Journey.* The original read "... remembering not to hide these qualities to protect other's egos. Use whichever one you like.)

This step is for pure celebration and acknowledgment of one's gifts, strengths and accomplishments. It brings balance to step five by focusing on our goodness, power, creativity and the thoughtful, caring things we have done. For some, this will be comfortable; for others it will be more difficult. One 16-step group calls this their celebration step and has a gathering afterwards. I have heard that women sometimes have a hard time with this step, they cringe and say with embarrassment, "I hope my list isn't too long," or "I feel as if I'm bragging" or "This seems so arrogant."

If you feel uneasy talking about your strengths, it might help to frame it this way: if our talents come from our creator, then to celebrate them is to celebrate creation. It doesn't mean we are better than someone, it simply means we celebrate our lives. When we affirm our strengths we can join together and use them collectively for good.

One time in a therapy group when women were resisting talking about strengths, saying they felt brazen or as if they were showing off, I said, "Okay, take a deep breath, count to ten and... presto! You're all corporate executives. Now talk." Their body language shifted and they started speaking in strong, deep voices, "Well let me tell you about this. "No, no I want to go first."

The second part of the step is to encourage people to remember their strengths and accomplishments and not hide these things to care-take others by acting weak, cutesy, ignorant, giggly, tough or seductive when someone of the opposite sex or a person we admire walks in the room. Imagine what would it be like if we stayed authentic, no matter who we are with.

❖ ◆ ❖ ◆ ❖

Exercises for Step 6:

l. *Bonding in power*

Write down a lot of wonderful, thoughtful, creative things you have done. Take turns having each member read her/his list to the group. If you need a reminder of your strengths, take your list home and put it in a place where you will see it daily.

Note: You might also use the ante up game where people forfeit a match or toothpick to a group 'pot' if he or she apologizes or qualifies what s/he says.

2. *Simply notice. (also can be used with step 7)*

a) Keep a journal for a week (or longer) of how you change your behavior around different people. Do you hide your power by getting giggly, scared, turning to mush, or otherwise losing your voice and your convictions with men, bosses, authority figures, women—anyone? Do you get tough, brazen or act super competent around certain people?

Simply observe your behavior with fascination and interest and listen to the messages in your brain: He won't like me if I say anything. She won't like me if she knows I'm broke. I'm acting super sweet because I'm really mad and I don't want it to show. I must not cry or act scared in front of my buddies because they'll put me down. She won't like me if I don't pay for dinner. Make a list and bring it back to group.

3. *Talking back to the junk mail in your head*

Write out all the thoughts and beliefs in your head that stop you from being true to yourself or following your dreams. Share what you have written down and say how you feel. Following this, have a brainstorming session on ways to counteract this junk mail. For example, If she doesn't like me having a small income, then I guess she's not for me. If they put me down when I am happy, successful and sober, then I'd better look for others to be around.

STEP 7

We become willing to let go of guilt, shame and any behavior that prevents us from loving ourselves and others.

"I stopped being the garbage can for other people's problems. I need to keep letting go of the guilty voice that tells me I have to heal everyone who is in my presence."

"As an alcoholic and product of my mother's abuse, I have been able to talk about my own abuse of my children. In the group I began to let go of the shame and guilt and connect with the grief I feel for the generations of maternal abuse in my family."

"I used this step to begin the rebirthing of my primary relationship. Each of us drew/wrote what kept us from loving ourselves and each other and then drew a picture of what we'd like to ultimately look like. Then we listened well and shared our writings/pictures with each other. Ten months later those pictures still don the bathroom wall where we can see them everyday. That was the beginning of incredible growth."

"I am learning to convert my shame and guilt into grief and then compassion."

Our culture and the Judeo/Christian tradition stress that we learn by suffering. Suffering has often been glorified. Empowerment is based upon a life-loving spirituality that suggests we are born blessed and that life is for joy, love and service.

Stop for a moment and take note of all the thoughts in your head that stop you from believing you have the right to be happy, to live with peace of mind and experience joy. Then ask yourself, how did all these thoughts get into your head?

This again leads us to understand internalized oppression. Any voice that keeps you from loving yourself and others is a form of internalized oppression. The voices could be instilled in your head from your mother, father, caregivers, clergy, medical institutions, teachers, government policies, laws, media, etc. If you are angry at yourself for taking in these oppressive teachings, remember it's a given that we collude with our oppressors as part of our survival. Sometimes it's a toss up between losing a job or losing self-esteem—a rotten, stressful choice. Being put in such a double bind is part of our oppression. Blaming yourself for the stress is also part of your internalized oppression.

Now ask yourself, what can I do to cast out these harmful beliefs and take steps to live my life fully? *It's important to understand the effects of our families, and of hierarchy and patriarchy, but, ultimately, to become healthy, productive adults, you need to live by your own beliefs.* Loving ourselves can be uncomfortable or feel as if we are committing a crime. But we're not. Giving birth to ourselves only feels like a crime because sexism, racism, classism and homophobia taught us we were defective, or not completely lovable. So rebel by telling yourself you get to heal, be well and take charge of your life. Then find the affirmation that fits for you: I get to heal and grow, or I deserve to feel good. Then take your affirmation and think it, dance it, write it, or sing it until it takes hold in every part of your being.

It may also help to know that when you start loving yourself or accepting the love of others, it will penetrate your heart and open up the old heartaches. And when the love comes in, the tears come out. So part of being willing to love yourself and others includes being willing to cry and grieve. It's hard to love ourselves more than we were loved as children, but we can learn.

Exercises for Step 7:

1. Take a piece of paper and title the page, *What does it mean to love myself?* Divide it into two columns: Behavior and Thoughts/Beliefs

Then take a minute to think about what it means to truly care for yourself. The behavior column could include things like, eating right, getting enough sleep, meditating, calling friends, taking a walk, taking time to paint, getting off a stressful committee, reading more, talking honestly with your partner about sex. The thoughts/beliefs columns could include saying phrases to yourself such as: I can learn to hold down a job. I can learn to play the harmonica. I can learn to have good friends. I am not stupid, I just need to study and learn. Even at my age I can get a good job. I can find a lover who is good to me. I can handle my anger. I can allow myself to experience my feelings. *I have the power to take charge of my life.*

Share the list in group and talk about your feelings.

2. *Taking steps to love yourself*

Using the list you made in exercise one, pick out the ones that have the most energy for you or seem most possible to do. Pick one or two plans to carry out in the following week. Write down all the details necessary to facilitate carrying out your plan. For example if it's winter in Minnesota and you commit to taking a walk, but don't have boots, plan to get some boots. Think of anything that could get in the way of carrying out your plan, and then deal with it. Don't say you will do macrobiotic cooking if you have no idea what it's about. Start with, I will buy a book on macrobiotic cooking. Be realistic.

Then do it! Report back to the group and make a plan for the following week.

3. *Using affirmations*

Find an affirmation that affirms your right to love yourself and others. Make sure it feels pithy and hits you in the gut. Some affirmations were suggested in the above text. Then go around the circle and have each person say their affirmation. If you like, have the group say the affirmation back to you, either one at a time or all together. (I call it the self-esteem chorus.)

4. *Living your affirmation.*

After you have found an affirmation that rings true for you, start working to integrate it into your life. Try various approaches to bring the meaning of the affirmation into your whole being.

You may want to take a daily walk and say the affirmation over and over for 20 minutes, four times a week. You may want to type it, write it, or make a collage that affirms your affirmation. Maybe you want to chant it while sitting and breathing deeply. Maybe you want to yell it to the Universe. Author's note: It was through the use of the affirmation, "I can love myself by writing this book.' that I was able to get unstuck and write *Women, Sex and Addiction.* I explain this process in depth in that book in Chapter 14.

STEP 8

We make a list of people we have harmed and people who have harmed us, and take steps to clear out negative energy by making amends and sharing our grievances in a respectful way.

"I am learning this step very slowly and deliberately. It has been a four or five year process to learn how to acknowledge, confront and discuss negative energy or harm, much less find a relationship or two or three where I can practice 'respectful' airing of such stuff."

"This has been a hard step for me. It meant acknowledging that my mother had been abusive and that my father had interfered with my normal sexual development. I look at how I have internalized the negative aspects of both my parents. Day by day I don't allow people to be abusive to me the way my mother was."

"This step is not a helpful part of my process right now. It's too scary. I need to grow a lot before I can do it."

"I used this step to affirm my... anger toward a physician who had been verbally abusive in the work place. Confronting this doc released my resentment."

This step helps us repair relationships and become free of negative connections to people. When we feel ashamed of how we treated someone, or have resentments toward someone who abused us, we are still connected to them in a negative way. On a path toward empowerment it is important to move toward inner clarity, which means clearing out conflict in old relationships and staying clear in new ones.

I cannot stress enough how much it costs us to hang onto unfinished business. It's like dense energy blocking up the body. Paradoxically we only know the price it extracts by the sense of relief and lightness we experience after taking care of a difficult situation. Even if a relationship or situation doesn't turn out the way we had hoped, when we put our heart and mind into speaking our truths with kindness, we can feel satisfied that we did the best we could.

Listing the people we have harmed: Note: For some people it is not helpful to focus on the harm they have done to others because they are depressed or feeling fragile and need affirmation and ego building. Also, when people are depressed or just trying to get their lives in order they often need to operate on a concrete basis before going inward—simply to get organized, get through the day, and think positive, hopeful thoughts. If this is the case, do the second part of this step first.

To look inside and think of the ways we have hurt others leads us to feel sorrow for our behavior and the pain it has caused someone. Stopping to think how we have hurt others can slowly help us realize the implications of our actions. If this is hard to do and you want to blame others, remember that blaming reflects a deep sense of power-lessness. It's like saying, I can't control what I do, think, feel, or drink so I blame others. To stop blaming is to take back one's power.

It is crucial when making an apology not to make excuses for yourself in the same breath. By explaining why you did what you did, you are covertly asking the other person to understand you. This is a form of re-victimization. (I have repeatedly seen people who sexually abused someone quickly say they are sorry then jump to make excuses by saying their life was hard, and so on. The person who was victimized is again put in the position of negating the pain of their behavior and understanding the one who perpetrated.) *The process is to say what you did, how you recognize it hurt the other person, and to say you are sorry for what you did.* Period. When you apologize it is important that the focus be on showing empathy to the person you have harmed. It will be a test of ego, but the results are well worth it. Later, if the person asks to know about your motivation or your situation, then you can tell them. Or, if after you have made a heartfelt apology, you can ask, Do you want to know what was going on with me when I hurt you?

Remembering ways we have harmed others often brings up shame and remorse: How could I have done that? I remember a mother who, when confronted by her adult daughter whom she had sexually and physically abused, broke down in tears and said, "I would give anything if it weren't true, but it is." Examining ourselves to see how we've harmed others often opens us to childhood abuse memories that may have been buried. Often, the harm we have done to others reflects the abuse perpetrated on us. Thus making amends can lead us to feel the full impact of our own abuse, which can help us heal and stop the cycle of abuse.

Apologizing and making amends is a long process that involves artful timing and sincerity. If we apologize without being sincere, it will not heal the other person. In fact, we will be using them again. Just making an apology is not enough if there is a long-term betrayal. A person may have to earn back the trust of the other person through being responsible and respectful. It is also important to decide if making amends is appropriate and respectful to the other person. If it is not wise or appropriate, you can role play it, talk about it or write a letter that you don't necessarily mail.

When we consider the harm we've done to others, we need to hold ourselves accountable, yet not beat on ourselves. We can make amends without grovelling. We can let ourselves feel the pain of being so separated from love and care that we harmed another person. In feeling this pain, we experience our effect on others which will help foster compassion within us. We can also remind ourselves that we are children of one and the same Creator and that we were acting out of our negative programming. The most important part is that we learn from past mistakes and commit ourselves to becoming more sensitive and compassionate toward other people. It's not enough to go on harming people and repeatedly say, I'm sorry.

It is also important to eventually forgive ourselves. While feeling guilt is an important signal that we have done something harmful, some people wallow in guilt as a way of pushing others away and not taking responsibility to grow up. It's almost like an addiction.

If you make an apology and grovel or wallow in guilt, you are again asking the other person to take care of you. I have seen parents or partners start crying and saying how bad they are, thus, once again shifting the attention back to themselves. Clients repeatedly talk about wishing their parents would recognize and apologize for what they have done, and then stop beating themselves up or acting guilty. It's even more wonderful when the parents or perpetrators take steps to heal and grow in their own lives.

Listing those who have harmed us: Acknowledging that people have harmed us and that we were not to blame can be a major step toward healing. Many people go through life feeling guilty or ashamed for how their caregivers treated them or for being raped, harassed or discriminated against. As children we all deserved safety, care and respect. When people do not recognize the abuse or discrimination for what it is, they often repeat the pattern by attracting people who use, abuse, or emotionally starve them and never realize they are being ripped off. They just know they don't feel very good, and often experience depression, anxiety, self-abuse, inner confusion and numerous addictions.

Making a list of ways you have been harmed or abused will help you get in touch with your anger, which is a survival reflex all people need to have. In other words, when we are threatened, the internal warning sign is a flash of anger. It alerts us to danger and helps us set boundaries: No, that's not all right with me; no, I deserve more than that; no, I want you to listen to me now and not interrupt. Feeling anger at someone who has harmed us can help us stand up for ourselves and remember not to get snookered back in with sweet talk and glib promises. (Of course this is not to be used as an excuse for being tyrannical.) Part of the routine socialization of women is to tell them their anger is ugly, unlovable or unfeminine. This is a way of teaching women to deny a basic survival reflex needed for self-protection. Many men are also taught to deny their anger, or taught to channel their hurt and pain into anger which is equally inappropriate. And remember, when you do not name a violation and state it as such, you will probably turn the anger inward or dump it on some other person who doesn't deserve it.

For those who tend to blame themselves for everything that goes wrong, remember that *blaming ourselves for being abused or saying it had no effect is a way to avoid the pain.* In a sense it is a form of control because we avoid our anger and never feel the grief of having been hurt. It also puts us at high risk for addictions. Many people fear expressing anger because they confuse it with rage and abuse, or are afraid it will consume them or go out of control. We need to learn there is an appropriate, non-blaming way to express anger.

Clearing out relationships through honest, respectful communication restores self-respect, and cracks through our isolation. Because addiction thrives in isolation, creating genuine human bonds is important. When we learn to make amends, we build a bridge that takes us out of our shame and reconnects us to others. When we hold others accountable for what they did to us, we gain our self-respect and develop our power.

Exercises for Step 8:

1. *Make amends to oneself*

Make a list of the ways you have abandoned, neglected or harmed yourself. How does this reflect how you were treated as a child? Then make amends to yourself and add statements such as, I will never shame myself this way again; I will never put myself in such danger again, and so on. (It doesn't mean you will stick to the affirmation perfectly. You do it to send an important message to your brain and start the process in motion.)

2. *Clear out negative connections with people*

a) Make two lists on two separate sheets of paper. Title one page, Ways I have harmed others, and title the other, Ways people have harmed me. It is possible to have the same person on both sides of the list, particularly with a partner. You may both have done harmful things to each other. Be as specific as possible and include all your feelings such as pain, sadness, anger, and hurt. For example: I harmed my daughter with my drinking and leaving her with others too often. My father harmed me with his violent rages. I learned to be afraid. As you write, keep listening inside and asking yourself, Have I said everything I need to say? A sign that you have said everything is when your mind starts to be quiet, your body relaxes and you feel a sense of clarity. For some people, it may take pages of writing over a period of days or weeks to start feeling clear.

Sometimes you may see a person's face and feel a blur of anger. Write it down. I'm angry. I feel hurt. You may not know why at the moment, but just let yourself have your feelings. You might want to draw or "dance" your feelings. After a while you may get more clear about the source of the anger. This sometimes takes a process of group or individual counseling, or taking time to meditate, pray or journal about it.

Before proceeding to talk with the other person, sort out how much of your anger is appropriate to that person and situation. Sometimes our anger at someone is intensified by anger from the past we haven't let ourselves feel. If you have an extremely hot or painful reaction, do a reality check with a couple of other people or a counselor before you talk to the person who has harmed you. (Be sure and talk to someone who you know is fair and doesn't automatically take your side against other people.)

b) Contact the person and ask to clear the air. If you reach agreement, set a time to talk. If this person is dangerous to you, you may want to write a letter, or do it by phone. If the other person is not willing, available, or alive, get a therapist or a couple of friends help you role play talking with the person. Again, this can include amends and/or the need to let them know how they hurt you.

c) If you clear the air and want to redefine the relationship, talk abut new expectations and ground rules. You might write them down before you get together to talk about it.

d) If you decide not to continue the relationship, say goodbye, acknowledge what you learned, grieve the loss, feel the relief, and move on. If the person was abusive to you but you have a hard time staying away, make a list of all the harmful consequences of being with that person. Read it daily to build up your resolve to stay away, and put the list where you can see it when you start to waiver. Working this step can be a long time process and involve numerous people.

STEP 9

We express love and gratitude to others and increasingly appreciate the wonder of life and the blessings we do have.

"Sometimes after the group meeting on this step, I feel very loving and caring. Then I go home and I hear myself say I love you more often to my life partner. I tend to appreciate her more...and the life I have."

"This step reminds me to say what my heart feels. I compliment and encourage the people who work with me more often."

"I had recently become aware of how much my focus is on the negative. It is important to periodically be grateful and notice and appreciate the beautiful and positive that happen, however small. Some of the group found it difficult to notice the good, but felt ...hope...because they had seen me when I was unable to be positive."

To look someone in the eyes and say genuinely, "You are special to me. You helped me, thanks," awakens our loving side and bonds us to other people. If God is love, then showing our love makes the presence of the spirit come alive within us and around us. Thus, expressing gratitude to people is a form of prayer that blesses both the giver and receiver. The thanks can be for anything that genuinely touched you— someone who was helpful, patient, tough, a good teacher, a good friend or lover.

We are repeatedly taught that we grow through suffering. (Which is not surprising since our culture perpetuates so much suffering.) In our shame-based culture we are trained to fix our eyes on violence, tragedy and scandal, which keeps an oppressive energy going. *I believe our strength is tested through suffering, but our spirit is fed by love.* Think of the many ways we grow through love. It helps us learn to give, receive, trust, be open, feel safe and develop compassion. Love helps us open our hearts and live though the pain of past abuse. Love will eventually heal our relationships between all living beings and the earth.

In my own experience with this step I decided to reconnect with a lot of people in my past going back to childhood. I wrote to a woman who had given me her tea set from her childhood 40 years earlier. I attended a high school reunion and apologized to my first boyfriend for suddenly leaving him and assured him it had nothing to do with him. I wrote letters to other old friends just to make contact and see how their life was progressing. I looked up a woman who had hired me to care for her children when I was a teenager, visited her in Florida and thanked her for her love and care. I cried as I wrote some of the letters because I was overwhelmed thinking of all the people who had cared for me (sometimes I forget almost totally). The net result was feeling more complete. Instead of my life feeling linear it was as if all the people in my past came alive, and I realized they were part of my present life because their love lived in me.

The second part of this step acknowledges the mystery and wonder of life along with the blessings we do have. Sometimes we get lost in negative thoughts and forget to remember our blessings. You may think you don't have any, that life has been absolutely rotten, but it's all relative. It can bring perspective to realize that we have a warm bed to sleep in, enough food, and people who care. This is not to minimize our problems, or put on a pollyanna face, but rather to lift the heaviness and restore balance to our perspective. One woman talked about momentary meditations that helped change her perspective on life, "...simply to remember to notice the leaves, trees, to hear a bird sing, or look at cloud formations."

Another way to tap into the wonder of life is to take an inward journey into your body. Imagine billions of cells at work regenerating themselves. Take a moment to listen to your heart beating away as it has all of your life. Wiggle your fingers, your toes, blink your eyes. Breathe deeply and fill yourself with life-giving air, remembering the miracle of creation that you are. (My book, *Finding Joy*, has many sections to help you tap into your joy.)

Eventually, being conscious of our blessings leads us to see, feel and love. It brings a sense of gratitude and joy and helps us be immersed in the present. It is a process of sensitizing ourselves to the positive, so we experience it more deeply, feel more filled up, and become gentler with ourselves. For many people it's a longtime learning process that takes daily practice.

This is a step to absorb into your daily life. To remember what you *do* have and to feel a sense of awe and wonder will ignite your heart and spirit and increase your capacity to give and receive love.

Exercises for Step 9:

1. *Love inventory*
   Make a list of all the people in your life who have been kind or helpful to you. Then write them letters, call them, thank them, and let them know how their love and care affected you.

2. *"Random acts of kindness"*
   Surprise some of your friends with flowers, notes or a message on their answering machine. Send a card to a child. Get a stack of postcards and say hello to old friends. (You could get a high school reunion list.) Do something for someone you don't know—put money in an expired parking meter, stand back and let someone go ahead of you in line if they seem restless, strike up a conversation with the person at a checkout counter and go beyond the routine conversation. Pay for a stranger's coffee at a restaurant.

3. *Gratitude circle*
   Go around the circle having each person say something they are grateful for.

Don't make lengthy explanations or give a lot of background information. Keep the circle going around and around. Feel what happens to the energy when we express gratitude.

4. *Write a thank you letter to yourself*
Write a letter to yourself as a child or younger adult thanking yourself for the strategies you developed to find pleasure, avoid pain and survive. Think of all the clever things you did, how you found pleasure and how you took care of yourself.

Read these letters in a group, or have someone read your letter to you, whichever you prefer.

5. *Go to the appendix and do the "I Understand" exercise on p. 119*

6. *Appreciation Circle*
Take time in your group to say what you appreciate about each other. Allow at least a half hour for eight to ten people. Include specific things the other person said or did and what you have learned from knowing them. When you are through, take a minute or two for silence to let all the words sink in. Then do something special to celebrate.

STEP 10

We learn to trust our reality and daily affirm that we see what we see,
we know what we know and we feel what we feel.

"This step is number 1. As a sexual abuse survivor and daughter of an alcoholic mother and a workaholic dad, my feelings never counted. My society also said that basing decisions on emotions was not adult, strong nor manly. Once I realized my perceptions were valid and did not have to be validated by an outside source, I was halfway home."

"This step has helped me separate from a boyfriend who knows how to lie convincingly without remorse...I tend to be manipulated with words."

"This step has helped me trust what I feel. I can now reach out to someone safe and check out my thoughts with them. Sometimes my reality comes right away, other times it is a process that takes a while."

"This step has helped me immensely in supporting my inner child and intuitive spiritual self. The more I acknowledge my own reality, the more I am able to respect and accept other people's realities, feelings and thoughts. In the group this was a powerful step that led to many significant discussions."

"I went to college and realized in my psych 101 class that normal people told people what they really thought. It may sound strange but I was absolutely amazed. I asked some friends if it were true; they said 'of course.' I knew then that I had some thinking to do, some changes to make. When a mouse begins to speak out, she often-times doesn't know how to do so politely, nor does she know how to back herself up."

"I have learned to 'trust my mistrust more...' I listen to myself and pay attention to my body signals. This step resulted in letting go of a friend that wasn't a friend."

According to the questionnaires, this step, along with numbers twelve and four were the most popular/impactful steps. It was difficult picking out quotes about this step because there were so many.

The purpose of this step is to develop trust in Self. To see what we see, feel what we feel, and know what we know is the antidote to internalized oppression. We were trained to see ourselves through the eyes of others—those who confine us to our limited roles.

In this step we grasp hold of our reality and learn to hang onto it. Yes, we listen to others, but we also listen to ourselves. We learn to notice behavior and not be conned by smooth words. If my gut tells me I'm being harmed, I pay attention to my gut. I don't have to have reasons to start believing the signals from my body. With this step, we build a healthy ego and self-trust. To get in touch with yourself keep asking: What really happened, How do I feel inside? Then listen for the response. It may take a while, or you might start arguing with yourself, but keep listening for your deepest truth. And, as mentioned before any spiritual truth will not cause harm.

When I originally wrote this step I included the phrase, *"when we are right we promptly admit it and refuse to back down."* I took it out because some people took it literally, stuck up for themselves and got into big fights. I would modify it to read, "refuse to back down inside of yourself." The point is to let yourself know when you feel clear and right inside and don't be swayed by sweet talk, hot political speeches or propaganda. Timing is important when you stand up for yourself, along with awareness of the possible consequences—so you won't be surprised. It's also important to remember you have a choice. You can speak up for yourself, or not, but in either case, hang onto your inner reality.

Exercises for Step 10:

1. Validate each other

NOTE: This step is not to be used to spur someone to violence or to feel righteous, rather to help people who are constantly doubting their reality to believe, themselves so they can become more assertive and stop swimming around in an emotional quagmire trying to figure out if their feelings are valid.

In a group take turns telling about experiences in which each person has difficulty believing their gut level reactions and have group members respond in a validating way.

For example, tell about a situation where you have a queasy feeling about something. "My boss started talking about his sex life and it felt icky." People respond, "Yeah, that's not appropriate, You're right, that's icky." A Native American says, "I didn't trust that business man telling us they want to use our land for businesses to create jobs for us." Others say, "Yes, look at the history. It sounds as if he's trying to con you." You can describe a situation and ask, "Am I imagining things or was I getting zapped/conned?"

2. Losing and finding ourselves

a) Go around a circle and tell of a time you knew what was best to do, and you couldn't get yourself to do it. First say what you did and then say the consequence.

Examples:
—"I wanted to tell Charlie I can't see him anymore, and when he called I invited him over to dinner instead." The consequence was that I hated myself and broke a date with a girlfriend who is now mad at me. I also spent a lot of money on dinner."
—"I knew I shouldn't go with Chris to buy cocaine, but I did it anyhow; and that's how I landed up in jail."
—"I wanted to say no to a promotion because it would take me away from my family, and I said yes anyhow. I am losing my relationship to my children, and my wife is talking about divorce."

b) To build resolve and strength for the next time a challenging situation happens, role play the situation differently. Say what you really wish you had said. Based on the above example with Charlie, have someone play Charlie. Say to him, "Charlie, as I see it, you've been dishonest with me. This relationship isn't working for me. I don't want to see you anymore." If you can't come up with words, have someone else talk back to "Charlie," then copy what they said until you find the words that feel right for you.

c) Pick a situation where you tend to lose your resolve. Brainstorm all the ways you could get help to do something differently the next time: In our example, plan to have someone come over when you call Charlie and have them hold your hand or make faces while you call; arrange to call someone before and after calling Charlie; write Charlie a letter; say affirmations for a week, I can let go of Charlie.

3. *Go around the room and have each person tell of a time he or she took a stand,* believed in themselves or took action in their own behalf. Cheer for each person as they tell their story. (Do this exercise often. It brings energy to a group, gives inspiration and reminds people of their strengths.)

4. *Listening for your truths (to be done in a group or alone)*
    To draw truths to your awareness, sit in a circle and have someone be the "leader." Take a moment for people to breathe deeply, relax and get quiet inside and perhaps close their eyes. Then have the leader say four or five times, "What is your truth?" Repeat the process either saying new thoughts that come up or repeat old thoughts that are still on your mind. Each person thinks to him or herself, "My truth is..." and speaks their answers out loud in random order: "I'm lonely; I want to get to know Alex." "I'm angry." "I feel good about the progress I've made." "I love my partner." "I'm unhappy in my job." "I'm afraid; I like where I am living." After a few minutes, the leader again says, "What is your truth?" Repeat the process several times. After you are done, sit in silence for a few minutes then process how this felt. You can also do this exercise in pairs.

    You can use "the truth is" to clarify a specific situation. Put the question in your mind and repeatedly say to yourself, "The truth is..." After the answer comes, the next question you put in your mind is, "What do I need to do about it?"

STEP 11

We promptly admit to mistakes and make amends when appropriate, but we do not say we are sorry for things we have not done and we do not cover up, analyze or take responsibility for the shortcomings of others.

"I have stopped taking more than my share of the responsibility in 'making up' or ending conflicts and am more willing to let others be accountable. I'm more willing to be in conflict and not have to 'fix' it."

"This step gave me the ability to recognize just how much covering up, analyzing and excusing goes on in relationships, especially where abuse is occurring. Abuse is just not okay anymore with me regardless of the reasons. IT'S NOT OKAY."

"This step was hard to face. When I stop analyzing others and trying to fix them, I become aware of a great emptiness and sadness inside of me."

I tried to get between my son and a chronic illness he had. This step has helped me see how my interfering in his life actually made things worse and gave him the message he was incompetent. My job is now to forgive myself (step 7)!"

In step 8 we talked about clearing out negative energy in old relationships; here we talk about staying honest in our current relationships.

Part of staying clear in relationships is by owning up to ways we are insensitive or hurtful. This restores trust with other people. Truly saying "I'm sorry" means acknowledging the harm we have caused. It is also important to listen quietly when someone says how your insensitive behavior has hurt them. (This doesn't mean you let yourself be unduly shamed and guilted—you can ask them to use "I" statements such as, "I felt _____ when you did _____" instead of saying "You did this," and "You did that.")

It's important to acknowledge your shortcomings gracefully, but not to grovel or hang on to guilt. This step was terrifying for me because I was sure if I admitted to doing something tacky or insensitive, the other person would hate me, never speak to me again or think of me as an awful person. Over time I learned that the opposite was true, but getting the words out initially felt like pulling a fish hook out of my throat.

Likewise it is important <u>not</u> to say you are sorry for things you have not done. In our hierarchical system oppressed people are routinely blamed for their oppression. Women repeatedly apologize and blame themselves for rape. Our culture colludes with such phrases as, "You asked for it. You shouldn't have been out so late at night," or "you shouldn't have let your date into your apartment." People in poverty are routinely blamed for their poverty instead of those with privilege looking at how they create a system that supports the rich and suppresses the poor. One aspect of internalized oppression is saying "I'm sorry," when in reality we are being abused or exploited and need to say so. It doesn't mean we use this as an excuse for not taking charge of our lives; it means that we don't blame ourselves for our oppression.

The second part of this step refers to people in dependent relationships who often spend hours a day analyzing or covering up for their partners. This is often a defense against having one's feelings and seeing the reality of the situation and saying, "It is not working. I need to get out. We need to get help." Stop and say to yourself, How do *I* feel about this situation? What's going inside of *me*? How is this putting *me* under a lot of stress? What do *I* need to say to clear the air? What do *I* need to do to move on? *No matter what happened to someone in childhood or what their situation was, or if they are under stress at work, they are responsible for their actions. That's the definition of being a grown-up. We don't make excuses. We take responsibility.*

Another aspect of this step is for people who repeatedly tell *What he or she did to me* stories. These stories are usually told with the tone of, *can you believe this!* When you tell these stories you take a one-up patronizing stance and ask the listener to bond with you against the other person or feel sorry for you. Telling a story as if you are surprised is also a way of staying in denial about the situation, especially if the other person's been doing the same thing for fifteen years! For most people it is also a way of avoiding anger. To change the pattern start expressing your feelings about what the other person did. I'm angry that my mother never calls me. I'm upset that my partner doesn't pay the bills on time. This will bring you into the present and into the arena *with* the other person instead of looking down from above (or up from below) as a non-participating observer.

Exercises for Step Eleven:

1. *A way to stop the cycle of analyzing others*
   Use "The truth is" exercise described in step 10.

2. *See mistakes as merely 'miss-takes'*
   Spend a week listening to the times you say, I should have, I would have, I could have.

   a) Write them down. Replace these thoughts with, I did or I didn't ...and this is how I feel about it and that's the way it is. (Remember, *I should have* is usually a defense against having your feelings.)

   b) Think of the lessons to be learned from miss-takes and what you can do to prevent them from happening again, or making them less often.

   c) Go through the list and check off the ones that you couldn't have controlled, or you simply made the best decisions you could with what you knew at the time. Come back to group and share your list. Talk about your feelings.

3. *Observe your analyzing and fix-it statements*

    a) Spend a week observing yourself and others analyzing, rationalizing, making up reasons, or excuses for something that happened. I call these "fix-it" statements. For example, Jane says, "I'm upset with myself at work, I'm so slow." A fix-it statement might be, "Oh I think you've got a lot of good things done. It's hard to work in this weather." A non-fix-it response would be, "Oh, you're upset; you feel like you're slow." In other words, intimate communication reflects back what the other person says and feels, it doesn't try to smooth over feelings.

    b) Make a list of fix-it statements. Be sure to indicate which were made by you as well as other people. Say how they felt in either case. Come back to group and share your list.

4. Make a list of all the times you tell a "what he or she did to me" or "what he or she did" story. Then go back and write in your feelings about it and how long it has been going on. Then promise yourself you will stop acting surprised and start being honest with the other person. Share this list with a group or another person.

5. *Empathic listening*

Make a list of conversations when you felt truly heard and understood by another person. Be specific about the words and tone they used. Share this collectively in a group. What common themes emerge?

STEP 12

We seek out situations, jobs, and people that affirm our intelligence, perceptions, and self-worth and avoid situations or people who are hurtful harmful, or demeaning to us.

"This is the step of all steps for people who are very dependent on others or have been in abusive relationships. It affirms you can let go of people and know you're okay."

"The group discussions about this step were extremely emotional."

"It never consciously occurred to me that I didn't have to spend the majority of my time with people in need, that I could spend my time by deciding to seek out people and jobs with health in mind."

"You mean I don't have to stick it out when I am being abused? I can just leave? I used to just stand there and take it when my ex-husband would verbally abuse me. Now I can hang up the phone or shut the door and not concern myself with whether his feelings are hurt."

"This step affirmed my decision to avoid relating with a past lover whose behaviors are not okay for me to be near."

Author's note: I've received many letters from people who said this step was life changing. It was a new concept to simply think you could be with people who are good for you, and stay away from people who drag you down. "You mean I don't have to go work it out, fight it through, try to fix him, and stay forever!" Women and men who had been in abusive relationships started feeling an inner sense of strength, affirming their right to take care of and protect themselves. One group stayed on this step for two months!

When we connect with people who affirm our intelligence and perceptions, it strengthens our belief in ourselves. This doesn't mean we close ourselves off to people with different belief systems. It means we stay away from people who constantly discount what we are saying, ignore us, want all the attention for themselves, and show no interest in our growth. It's hard enough to do the healing journey with support and care, it's incredibly difficult or impossible when someone is pulling us backwards. Instead of growing, we spend all our energy just treading water. If it is necessary to be in a difficult situation—nurturing a dying parent or caring for difficult children for example—try to balance the scale by doing things that fill you up.

I suggest people think in terms of energy readings. Think of a light meter going from density to light, or from energy drain to energy charge. Then take energy readings after being with a person, being in a meeting, watching a TV program, or reading a book. Do you feel light, peaceful, invigorated and clear, or do you feel drained, dense, agitated and heavy? We think in terms of a car using up a certain amount of gas and then needing a refill, but we seldom think of people as energy fields needing fuel for life. Many people are trying to run on an empty tank and wearing themselves out in the process or depending on stimulants.

When we make decisions based on energy readings, we can simplify life. We simply stop and ask ourselves, Will this nurture me or deplete me? Do I really want to do it? Unfortunately in our system, many people are swamped in negative energy—welfare system, poor housing, dreary jobs. But we all have some choices about friends, what we watch on TV, what we read and how we think. Every choice we make matters.

The essence is this: *go toward whatever feels light or energizes you, and avoid whatever feels dense and drags you down. Light energy is fire energy, the source of transformation.*

Exercises for Step 12:

1. Check your energy sources

    a) Imagine an energy meter inside you—energy drain to energy charge—on a scale of one to ten. Then scan a day on an hour-to-hour basis, giving each hour a rating. Include the time you sleep. What is your score? The possible high energy charge for a 24-hour period is 240. After that, scan your week in a broader sense. What patterns do you see? How well are you balancing the intake and output of your energy? If this is too complicated, reflect back over the day and do an energy assessment of various activities in the day.

    b) Do the above exercise throughout the week keeping notes on a scale of 1-10 of all the situations in your life. Make particular note of the highs and lows. Come back and share it in group.

    c) Spend a week consciously adding things to you life that charge your energy. Check into your group with the results.

2. What feels good, and why?
Think of a situation in which you felt affirmed, listened to, validated and made to feel happy about who you are. Be as specific as possible in recounting exactly what was said or done that helped you feel this way? What was the communication like? What was the tone of voice like? Eye contact? What can you learn from this experience?

3. Practice energy readings
Pair up. Have someone name situations and answer only with an energy rating from one to ten. Questions could be: What you ate for dinner last night. Last time you made love/had sex. Your job. Your roommate. Your neighbor. The state of your bedroom closet. Answer immediately without thinking. Just say whatever comes up on a scale of one to ten.

4. *Opting Out...Saying "NO"*

Give yourself permission to refuse an invitation to an event that you know will make you feel uncomfortable. Make a list of what you have to lose and what you have to gain. Then let yourself hear all the voices that dance in your head. Come back to group and tell about your experience.

5. *Say Yes to something new*

Break through an old barrier, push through your resistance, and say yes to something new. Many people have difficulty going new places, inviting someone to dinner, meeting new people, attending social events, lectures, workshops, or community gatherings. Even if it turns out to be boring, or a drag, you will have broken an internal barrier and freed yourself from fear. Keep doing this. (You never know who you'll meet or what you'll learn, but everytime I do this I learn something new...it's also how I met my life partner!)

STEP 13

We take steps to heal our physical bodies, organize our lives, reduce stress, and have fun.

"I took off from work for 11 months, working only part-time to re-establish the sense I once had of myself as a child in school with summers off. I gave up workaholism."

"I now exercise frequently and have taken up sports I used to envy others for doing. I plan for restful hours, not moments. I flow with the energy present in my body and environment...As a result I am more productive, stress-free and happier than I ever thought possible."

"Finding out about allergies and food sensitivities have been core to my sobriety and peace of mind. I had systemic yeast problems that were at the root of my constant cravings for alcohol and sugar. I didn't need a moral inventory I needed to heal my body!"

"In the group we experienced giving ourselves permission to be gentle with ourselves. It was liberating and scary—as if there was some universal time clock and we had clocked out too early. Would we be caught? What would the consequences be?"

A life-loving/creative spirituality seeks to create harmony and balance between body, mind, and spirit. Restoring the body to a healthy balance is one important way to bring balance to a person at all levels. Many people have cravings for addictive substances because their body ecology is tremendously out of balance. The answer is to get nutritional counseling and possibly supplements from a practitioner who understands the biochemical connection to substance cravings.

Exercise and learning to monitor one's thoughts are also important to this process. Numerous books on cognitive therapy help this process including *Feeling Good* by David Burns and my book, *Finding Joy.*

Getting ourselves into balance is important for many reasons. When we feel physically well, we have more psychological resilience. As a result we tend to be less explosive, less depressed, and more able to take on the challenges of life and heal our pain from the past. (For more information, there is a chapter called "The Physical Connection" in *Many Roads, One Journey.* I also recommend Joan Mathews-Larson's, *Seven Weeks to Sobriety,* which includes a chapter on depression.)

In terms of reducing stress, one way to start is to slow down the pace of your life. Start cutting unnecessary meetings, words and possessions out of your life. Many people are unrealistic about planning their time and try to cram too much into one day. If they had left out just one thing, there would have been time for everything. Scheduling things too closely leaves people hurrying from one place to another, being breathless and being late. For some people, being busy is itself addictive and a huge defense against underlying feelings.

The other place to simplify your life is in your conversations. An important step on the path to empowerment is to speak clearly, simply, put a period at the end of a sentence and take a breath. Most people can only hear one or two sentences at a time. If you tend to talk on and on, practice reducing sentences to basics: "Yes," "No." "I want...," "I need...," "I'd like to ...," "I don't want to...," "Maybe," "I'll let you know." Most of all breathe between sentences and notice how the other person is reacting. Many people keep talking or repeat themselves as a nervous habit to fill in the empty spaces. Try letting the empty spaces be there. Speaking takes energy and listening to someone who uses 100 words when 10 would do is exhausting.

Many people hold their breath *while* they talk. It's often a defense against being connected emotionally to what you are saying, and it often feels flat or disconnected to the listener. If you do this, practice breathing out and talking from down in your solar plexus and belly. Say one sentence then stop to release your breath again. See how it feels.

Getting organized is another part of reducing stress. The idea is to reach for something and have it there. In *Clutters Last Stand,* Don Aslett writes: "There is a wisdom in letting go of things that clutter and choke your life...Most of us never taste the new, the fresh, the zestful because we have our heads and hearts gripped clear to the quick in clutter...*Hanging on will hang you.*"

Having fun and celebration are also central to a life loving/creative spirituality. Laughter and joy spark our energy. Even if life is difficult or you are going through a difficult time, try to take a break, be spontaneous, celebrate something, or go out and have a good time.

The important word is balance. We renew our creative energy by having a wide array of experiences and stimulation balanced with quiet and solitude. Let go of the thought that if you aren't doing something *productive,* you're bad. Some people never truly rest. They feel guilty at the mere thought of having a mindless, happy, task-free day, doing whatever comes to mind. It *is* productive to your spirit, immune system, and peace of mind to relax, have fun and play.

Exercises for Step 13:

1. *Learn to lovefoods that love you back. (See Yin Yang Eating Worksheet on page 125)*
    a) Fill out the worksheet with or without using the Yin Yang Chart. The point is to make connection between what you eat, how you feel, and how you sleep.
    b) Variation: For one or two weeks, eat things that are at the extremes of the chart if this is your current diet and then for two or three weeks, eat foods in the one, two, three range of the chart and see how you feel. Typically as

you eat nearer the center of the chart, food cravings will diminish and you will feel more relaxed and less jumpy. Note: Some people notice the differences immediately, for others it takes longer.

2. *Being quiet*

   a) Spend more time without the radio, TV or phone calls. Don't turn on the TV, or radio, or grab the paper the minute you walk in the house. Cook, eat, and drive in silence constantly tuning into your breathing. Don't fill all the empty places with phone calls. Keep track of your feelings and report back to the group.

   b) Make a weekly schedule of times when you will sit and do nothing with no music, phone calls, or interruptions. Just sit and breathe, look out the window and relax. It could be five 10-minute intervals.

Tell the group about your experience: what worked, what resistence you felt, how it felt, and what went through your mind. (Keep at it)

3. *Conscious breathing*

Conscious breathing is core to the spiritual journey. There are many techniques—Transcendental Meditation (TM), kundalini breathing, etc. Basically you can tune into your breathing. Follow your breath going in and out, in and out. Notice what happens when you slow down your breathing or take a deeper breath and hold it just a bit and release it more slowly than you might naturally. Notice when you keep your breath going in a continuous unbroken flow. While you are breathing, be aware of the clutter/chatter in your mind but don't give it willing attention. Just keep tuned in to your breathing. You could also add an affirmation or a sound.

4. *Listing your pleasures*

   a) Make a list of all the things that bring you pleasure. Go around the circle and tell the others. Notice how you feel throughout this process.

   b) Then re-read the list and go around the group saying all the things you would like to learn to do, or do more of.

STEP 14

We seek to find our inward calling, and develop the will and wisdom to follow it.

"This step has helped me make a commitment to my art work [even though] some of my friends and family would prefer to see me in a conventional and more secure occupation."

"I had been a mechanical drafter for 10 years—then it went computerized on me. I started going to school to "adapt"—but dropped out realizing that I wasn't doing what I wanted. I will be going to school for AODA counseling soon."

"Following my calling is the core of my spirituality. It's about listening deeply for the little truths as well as the big ones, like what I want to wear or who I want to spend time with? The more I live at one with my beliefs, the better I feel. It isn't always easy, and I've had to let go of places and people and things, but there is a sense of going home to some wonderful place."

In this step we go from *willingness* to *action* based on our own truths. Quakers call it following their inner calling. The toughest part of the spiritual journey is *living* our beliefs. Many preach, write, and talk a good line. But those who live their beliefs are often quiet or modest about it.

The first step is to listen inwardly on a daily basis so we are in touch with our heart's desire and our purpose. As this becomes known to us, the challenge of the journey is to move closer to these values and beliefs. It's important not to reach for some mythical ideal of purity. The idea is to find our dreams, sort through our values, and journey toward them with a lightness of spirit, accepting our blunders and slips along the way. We also need to accept that our values may change over time.

The path is usually a series of small steps that may include deciding to: take a walk, attend a workshop, drop in on a neighbor, find a new career, work less, work more, give up a fancy high paying job, go for a better job, give up drug dealing, go back to school, become sexually involved, leave a sexual relationship, take a vacation, or rest for a few days at home. It can involve loss, grief, relief, and joy. At another level it is about staying tuned into ourselves. One woman called it "Minute to minute honesty."

A decision we *make* differs subtley from one that *happens internally.* In both cases we can make lists, talk about possibilities and weigh all possible outcomes. When we *make* a decision, we consciously decide on one alternative. We may feel conflicted about the decision, but we go ahead with it. It seems to be the best we can come up with. Allowing a decision to *happen* is like allowing the truth to surface. We put the information in our mind and heart, then let go of the outcome and wait until the decision comes clear for us. It's like putting something on the back burner and letting it simmer. I remember after my divorce, Knowing that I would be moving to some new place. I went about my life, meeting people, and getting involved in various activities. Through a series of events the path opened, and I was led to know where to move—London, England, to study piano. We don't always have the luxury of time to do this, but when possible, try to ingest information then let go of the decision and ask the Universe/God/Goddess to let you know what's true or right for you... Then go about life staying open to people, events, activities, books. Often you will have an experience or read something that will trigger the answer coming clear.

Finding our inner voice and gaining courage to live by our beliefs can be scary. This is where faith and trust enter the picture. To have the courage to follow our calling is sometimes a leap of faith—yet living by our truths is all we ultimately have in life.

Exercises for Step 14:

1. *Clear decisions*

   Go around the circle and talk about times that you felt really clear about a decision that turned out to be a good choice. What process did you use to reach the decision? Distinguish if you *made* the decision or allowed it to *happen*.

   After everyone has spoken, brainstorm in the group to see if there are common patterns in people's decision-making processes.

2. *Sorting out the inner voices*

   Go around the circle and tell how you know when your wise side is speaking, and when your addictive/dependent side is speaking. Make a list as group members speak, and then look for patterns. (Note: the addictive dependent side is usually driven by fear or a desire to escape feelings.)

3. *Sorting out reality from fantasy*

   Have a group discussion about recognizing when you are staying in reality, and when you are drifting off into a dream world, being impractical or unrealistic. Give concrete examples, including the thoughts that usually precede your drifting off.

   How does the dream world bring comfort? How does it keep you from improving your life? When is daydreaming useful?

4. *Create a Vision*

   a) Close your eyes, turn inward, focus on your breathing, and slowly relax every part of your body. Then imagine having your life exactly how you would like it to be, based only on things you have control of. What is it like? (Some questions you could ask: Where am I living? What do my surroundings look like? Who am I relating to? How do I feel inside? What kind of work do I do? What kinds of activities am I engaging in all day long? What kind of contribution am I making to other people, to my community, the planet?)

b) Once you have a vision of what you want, the next step is to chart your course for getting there. Ask yourself on a daily basis, *What am I doing today to live the way I want to live?* Do this over a period of time—a week, a month—and keep telling yourself it is a daily process. There is no magic cure, no flight over the rainbow, no leaping from despair to joy. *Healing and becoming whole is a series of small, ordinary, daily steps mingled with some big risks.* Paradoxically as you do this, don't lose sight of being tuned into everyday pleasures. It's a dance between living now and moving toward your values.

STEP 15

We accept the ups and downs of life as natural events that can be used as lessons for our growth.

"It's important for me to accept the fluctuations of mood in daily life. I no longer feel compelled to help others 'feel better.'"

"In my years experience in 12-step groups I kept hearing, stick with us you will be joyful, happy and free. After my first 3 or 4 years...it just wasn't happening. Everytime I would go through my 'downs,' I would think I was not working the program hard enough, why weren't the promises coming true for me. It made me crazy !!!!!!. This step has helped me see that life just 'is.' Things happen—the good and the bad. I have finally realized that I can do sadness and I will be okay. I can do anger and I will keep living."

"It reminds us to ride the waves a bit and not worry about getting wet. It implies that there is an order or power beyond our complete control."

"I never realized ups and down were 'natural'—if things went bad, I became afraid I was going to be destroyed. This step helps me keep a perspective on hard times."

The recovery and new age movements have led many people to pathologize life by becoming vigilant and worried about sadness, grief, anger, loss, loneliness, blue days, happy days, or times of confusion. It's important to remember that life is not a sickness to overcome. As one woman in a "recovery" group put it, "I sometimes feel as if I'm this thing in need of constant fixing." I call it recovery narcissism.

All people on the planet go through gradations of being up and down. While it is important in the first stages of uncovering from an addiction to pay careful attention to cues that might lead to relapse, it is also important not to stay perpetually engrossed in oneself. In recovery and new age groups you often hear people talk as if there is a God in heaven controlling every little thing that happens, endowing it with meaning. When people get narcissistic about recovery, they close themselves into a narrow world and lose touch with the most healing force that exists—getting outside oneself, relishing beauty, expanding one's self-definition, and engaging in community efforts that help others.

Life has its ups and downs. Our moods and feelings sometimes wax and wane with the moon, our hormonal cycles, and with the seasons. There is an ebb and flow to all things. The wisdom lies in distinguishing between knowing when it's time to introspect and when it's time to take a deep breath, go for a walk, enjoy a movie and let oneself be. Again, the word balance comes into play. It's one thing to be frozen up and out of touch with yourself, it's another to be constantly self-absorbed.

Part of development into maturity is to be able to *observe* your personal soap operas and not drown in them. Our ups and downs matter, but in the cosmic scheme of things, they're not serious, they come and go. The ups of life can be used as lessons for our growth, but it's always a choice. We don't have to add *deep meaning* to everything that happens to us. Very often when people are tired, depressed or over worked, the goblins dancing in their minds will disappear if they get some sleep, eat well, add some pleasure to their lives and get some exercise. Often I suggest to people to try this first and then, if "whatever" is still bothering them, they can explore it.

Exercises for Step 15:

1. *It matters...but it's not serious*
   Think of a situation that got you very upset (past or present). Bring it back to mind—feelings and all. On a piece of paper make two columns: "It matters" and "It's not serious." Think of your situation and write down all the ways it matters, (It's upsetting. It made me late. It cost money, etc.) then list all the ways it is not cosmically serious (It won't make headline news. The moon will still rise. The buses will still run and cows will still moo...and it won't be of great significance when it's time to write my obituary.)

   In a group go around and share what you have written in both columns. Which side do you need to pay more attention to?

2. *Irritation/Anger notebook*
   Exercises two and three are for people who equivocate, won't take a stand or refuses a clear opinion without apologizing or explaining.

   Keep a notebook for a week and let yourself write down everything you don't like or everything that makes you mad. Write as if you are on your soap box. Be dramatic. Say it with vigor, and don't qualify anything you write. Use phrases like, "I can't stand it when_____." " I think it's so stupid when_____."

   In the group:
   a) Share what you wrote (optional)

   b) Say how you felt writing.

   c) Tell about any difficulty you had doing this exercise—the arguments in your head that tried to stop you.

3. *I like notebook*
   Do the same as excercise two starting with statements such as, I like _____, I enjoy _____, I'm happy when _____, I feel hope when _____.

4. *Speaking without justification.*
   Circle around a group saying things you like and things you don't like. Use the

form, "I like_____." and, "I don't like_____." Don't explain or qualify what you say. For example you could say, "I like bananas." Avoid saying things like, "I like bananas because they are full of potassium and with menopause coming on they are especially good for my muscles." (You could include the ante up game of contributing matches or toothpicks when people start qualifying or explaining things.)

STEP 16

***We grow in awareness that we are sacred beings,
interrelated with all living things, and we contribute
to restoring peace and balance on the planet.***

"I have felt most connected when I am working in the community on issues I believe in. This step has helped me know that I am a sacred being. It has helped me not just take my gifts to the recovery community, but to the great 'Circle of Life' where all are connected."

"I'm just starting to be able to do something inspired by this step. I'm doing what I can do to support the 16-step groups. I'm getting people together to see how this empowerment model can be brought into prisons and residential addiction recovery centers. The response has been wonderful."

"At first the thought of having an impact in the world seemed overwhelming. Who me? But last week a friend said to me. 'I was feeling upset with a friend and being a wimp, then I thought of how you've learned to stand up for yourself and I spoke out.' I realized that everything we do and say matters, and that by getting stronger, I am having an impact in the world."

As our lives include more direction, love, joy, happiness and connection to others, we start experiencing ourselves as part of a web that includes all life. We realize that none of us are isolated beings: our words, thoughts, deeds and use of the world's resources are all deeply interconnected. We no longer compartmentalize love as something we are seeking outside ourselves, rather we come to dwell in love. As we create balance in our lives we are more acutely aware of the need for balance in the world between all people, animals, plants, air water and other natural resources.

The spiritual journey inevitably kindles the desire to reach out to others and be a force for good on the planet. We don't help others in order to look good, we do it because we feel called to do so. It is a natural process that evolves as we feel abundance in our lives. At a basic level, we improve the world by being a loving, open, authentic human being.

At another level, we can become involved in being of help to all living things—people, animals and natural resources. In speaking of Creation theology, which is similar to a life-loving/creative spirituality, Matthew Fox says, "It's not enough to awaken the heart and right brain if you don't also put that energy to work relieving the suffering of the world." The massive addiction problems people suffer reflect a culture in denial and in pain. It's all interrelated.

An important aspect of this step is evaluating how we live in relationship to our natural resources. Are we using more resources than we need? Are we buying more than we need? I am not saying that one should become austere or not have some beautiful possessions, but I am saying that as part of the earth's ecosystem, we need to be part of restoring balance between what grows naturally on the planet and what we consume. We need to be aware of the toxic effects of chemicals in the rivers and in the earth and be aware of our part. We need to be aware of the legacy we are leaving for the generations to come, and live accordingly.

In the traditional 12th step people were encouraged to reach out to other alcoholics. Now we extend that step and reach out wherever there is need. Thus we move beyond our identity with ourselves, our families, our support group, and reconnect with the broader community and with the earth as a force for good. We shed the label addict, and become a human being—a spirit, a life, a seeker, a friend.

Exercises for Step 16:

1. Remembering the good times
   a) Think of a time when someone reached out with love and kindness or surprised you with something wonderful without expecting anything in return. (It can be when you were feeling good or when you were feeling lousy or in need.) If you can't think of such a time, imagine a time when you wanted someone to reach out to you and what you wish they would have said.

   Tell the story to your group.

   b) Go around the circle and describe a time when you reached out to another person or surprised them with something nice, asking nothing in return.

2. Get a group of people from different backgrounds together
Arrange to meet for several consecutive weeks. At the first meeting have some form of get acquainted exercise, then have everyone draw their family of origin on a big sheet of paper using crayons, markers or paints. On consecutive weeks, taking an hour or two per person, have people introduce their family and tell about their lives.

Once everyone has done this you could spend an evening and have people talk about the major turning points in their lives. (Or get together and decide on a format for telling about yourselves. Let the process arise from the people who get together. What would they like to talk about. Generally it is best to have a format or a particular subject.)

3. Community involvement
Make a list of the causes that you feel strongest about. Talk about them in the group. Include what you have done about the causes that interest you or say what you would like to do about them. If you want to be more involved and don't know how to start, have the group brainstorm with you.

4. *Seven Generation Consciousness*

In Native American cultures decisions were based on the impact the action would have on the seven generations to follow. Imagine if everyday you and those around you considered what they ate, how much energy they consumed, what they said, what they purchased in context of its impact on children of this and future generations. How might you change your life? Talk about this in your group. Then do everything you can to live according to your beliefs.

5. *Attend the Dances for Universal Peace*

The Dances for Universal Peace are a profound means for personal and planetary healing and spiritual growth. They are available to all comers in many cities and towns through the United States and other parts of the world. Performed in a circle, often with ever changing partners, the Dances include songs and chants from all major spiritual traditions which are sung to movements that emanate from the spirit and feeling of the words. They bring a profound integration of body, mind and spirit when done repeatedly. What I like personally about the Dances are the sense of joy, beauty, adoration, peacefulness and connection they bring. It's like dancing in the center of a prayer for peace that brings spirit into my heart, calms me down, fills me up, clears my mind and supports me in all that I do.

To find out about resources in your area you can contact:

Peaceworks
International Center for the Dances of Universal Peace
444 N.E. Ravenna Blvd. Suite 306
Seattle, WA 98115-6467 U.S.A.
Phone (206) 522-4353

The Trauma-Addiction Connection
Making Sense of Chaos

The 16-Step program has helped me look at the trauma which drove me to addiction. To deal on the deepest level of my foundation--the pain and tragedy. To speak about it, feel it, and share it with others has allowed me room to let go of the need to medicate or numb myself.

Kelley G— a 16-step group member

Treating substance abuse and other addictions without addressing the underlying trauma, abuse, violence or neglect is often ineffective or laboriously slow. People are left at high risk for relapse, switching addictions, white-knuckling sobriety, chaotic relationships, and continued depression and anxiety. The use of addictive substances or behaviors is often an attempt to regulate or manage extreme emotions or anxiety, anesthetize painful memories, soothe loneliness, hide from shame, feel a sense of belonging, relax, or feel elated and happy. Lonely? Eat for comfort, or have sex to be touched. Overwhelmed with painful memories? Use drugs or numb out to obliterate reality. Anxious at social gatherings? Smoke pot before you go out or drink alcohol. Ashamed of being poor, a minority person, gay, or lesbian? Repeatedly hide your true identity and drink, eat, get depressed, or shop. Feel life is hopeless? Descend into a blur of drugs and sex.

The 16-step program goes to the heart of the issues underlying addiction by systematically addressing many of the well-researched criteria for overcoming trauma

The criteria addressed in the 16-step empowerment approach help people:

❖ **Become** able to give and receive comfort and develop safe and secure relationships with self and others

❖ **Gain** a sense of mastery over daily aspects of one's life—money, relationships, emotions

❖ **Develop** a strong core sense of self –explore one's strengths and talents and ability to be grounded

❖ **Experience and contain** a wide range of emotions and feelings

❖ **Reconnect** with the signals of the body

❖ **Access and trust** one's inner wisdom

❖ **See situations in current time** as opposed to being in trance states from the past

❖ **Value self care**--sleep, rest, exercise, healthy eating habits, personal hygiene

❖ **Learn** to set appropriate boundaries in order to manage one's emotions and energy

❖ **Tap into** one's creativity

❖ **Appreciate and be comfortable** with differences

❖ **Develop a frustration tolerance** in the interest of learning and taking on new tasks

❖ **Develop an expansive concept of self and others** that moves beyond labels

❖ **Experience fascination, awe, wonder and joy**

Making the link between trauma, neglect, violence and addiction is a crucial and powerful aspect of the 16-step model. In interviewing women in 16-step groups, nearly all said they had felt "crazy" as a result of incest and abuse because what they were told by their supposed care givers clashed with their experience of terror, fear, and loneliness. It takes awareness and effort to see through one's own eyes and get past self deprecating thoughts such as I deserved it, I'm defective, unlovable or shameful. Understanding that people use addictive substances as an attempt to manage a chaotic inner world helps people make sense of their behavior, feelings, and current experience. As one woman in a homeless treatment program said in response to my hand-out, Responses to Trauma, "This makes so much sense. I thought I was just this stupid, bad person who had all these addictions. I never thought about it having something to do with all the horrible stuff in my childhood." Making sense of patterns that were set in place in childhood is a powerful antidote to shame.

THE NATURE OF TRAUMA

Neurons which fire together, wire together
Donald Hebb, Canadian physician-psychologist

Trauma is a physical and emotional response in the body to a situation, event, or experience that a person is not able to process, understand, or handle. Trauma can be a single event or a chronic violation to self that feels overwhelming, terrifying, unbearable, or deeply shaming. It's a blow to the self or the ego that leaves a person stunned, frightened, terrified, confused or chaotic inside. The body reacts at every level: muscles tighten, palms sweat, breathing gets tight, the mind dissociates, the body goes numb or the voice is lost. There can be a wide range of physical sensations such as tingling in the arms, burning in the chest, constriction in the throat, or tension in the stomach. Repeated firing or stimulation of these physiological systems including the secretion of cortisol--a stress hormone--weakens the immune system and puts people at high risk for depression and illness.

Trauma can also be insidious in that the prolonged experience of being shamed, guilted, neglected, invalidated, dismissed, or threatened with abandonment can lead to physiological and psychological disruptions and numbing. One woman put it this way: "I was always wilting with hurt and shame from their constant criticism and put downs. They never hit me but I would have this sickening disgust inside and feel total hated for myself. I felt suicidal for years." Chronic shaming can result in a limited sense of deservedness that leads to inertia, ambivalence, difficulty taking action, and a mind ranting with critics and censors. Conflicting signals from a parent can also lead to confusion and a sense of betrayal. For example, if a mother is kind to her child when they are together, but does not protect her in the presence of the father-figure when he beats or shames her, the child and may develop highly anxious ambivalent feelings toward others.

Physical trauma can include hitting, kicking, beating, sexual violation, throwing, pushing, shoving, and all forms of torture. Emotional trauma can include constant threats of abandonment, neglect, yelling, locking children in confined spaces, killing a child's pet, withholding food, merciless teasing, shaming, intimidating, manipulating with guilt, being dismissive, unresponsive, invalidating, intrusive, and acts devoid of empathy or attunement. Trauma responses, can also stem from a highly inconsistent parent who is caring one moment and dismissive, absent, or abusive the next, leaving a child in perpetual fear. Severe unpredictability is an aspect of terrorism.

Trauma as Disregulation. Trauma is often referred to as resulting in disregulation of all systems of the body. This includes our thoughts, emotions, mental states, and physiology which create an interwoven matrix of connections. To explain: think of a thermostat. Its purpose is to keep the temperature steady and comfortable. It pulls extremes toward a balance point by turning up the heat if it's cold and turning it down if it's hot. If the thermostat is broken or disregulated, the heat might go up to 80 followed by the air conditioning taking it down to 50. Translated to human experience, people face similar tasks with extremely different physiological and emotional thermostats. For example, when a person with a stable emotional and physiological thermostat takes on a challenging task such as fixing a bicycle for the first time, the thoughts might go like this: Let's see, what seems to be the problem, hmm, what needs to happen (looks the situation over). Well that doesn't seem to work, what else could I try? Let's try this. Hmm. That's better. I'm not sure about this. Maybe I should ask my neighbor. He's good at this." On a scale of 1–10 their frustration/agitation level might hit 3 or 4 after a half hour of trying, at which time the person takes a break, calls someone and then comes back. A person with a disregulated inner world approaches the same task with thoughts such as, "Oh god I don't know if I can do this, (their physiological response immediately shoots up to an agitations level of 6 which makes it difficult to focus), why do I have to do this? Okay, let's see. Shit that doesn't fit right. That damn thing doesn't work. Why do I always have to do these impossible things! Nobody cares about me. (kicks the bike), to hell with it."

Diagram 1. Two images of an agitated system—it could apply to breathing, heart rate, mental confusion, muscle tension, anger and agitated thoughts. Imagine trying to be reasonable in a difficult conversation or taking on a challenging task when experiencing this inner turmoil. Note your physical response as you look at these diagrams.

Diagram 2 Here is an image of a well regulated system that has a steady flow with regard to pulse, respiration and emotions. Imagine having this internal experience when having a conflict, taking on a task, or being faced with a stressful situation.

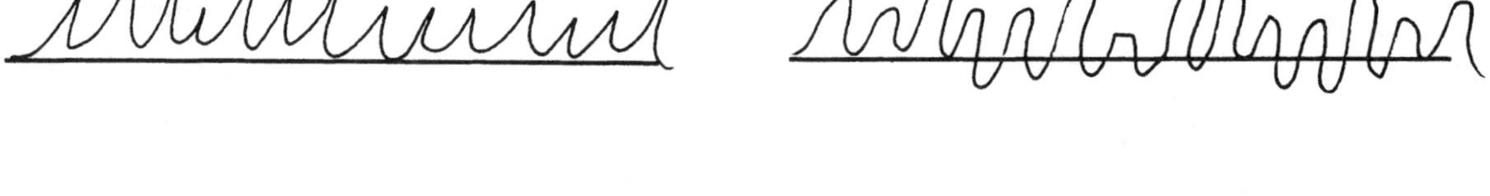

It's easy to imagine that someone who feels down much of the time wants uppers, while someone who feel emotionally volatile or has a fear of strong emotions may prefer marijuana or other depressants, and someone who feels nothing much may want a stimulant drug or dangerous activity that brings an adrenaline rush to feel alive.

Some people tend to feel down much of the time, others ricochet between lows and highs, and still others feel flat emotionally. Here's where the expression "drug of choice" needs to be turned around. In reality, the drug chooses you. Whatever works to lift you up, calm you down or help you feel alive is what your physiology will choose. This can apply to all forms of eating disorders, over work, gambling, and sex, as well as alcohol and other drugs. A feedback loop gets established in the brain that brings up the thoughts of whatever substance or behavior alleviates the turbulence or numbed out feelings. This underlies the phrase "the drug was *calling* me." The "calling" comes from the body going into withdrawal and wanting relief.

We learn to care for ourselves by being cared for. Attentive, warm, and attuned parents help infants feel safe, trusting, and relaxed. People with chronic addictions rarely had a secure attachment to a loving parent in a stable, safe household. Early deprivation or trauma often results in a deep sense of feeling isolated, unsafe, ashamed, and needing to go it alone in the world. This puts people at high risk for addictions—anything to fill the emptiness and stop the torment of feeling unlovable or worthless. When people describe their inner experience, it is often that of being empty, alone, confused, jumbled, helpless or desperate. As a result, instead of relationships that soothe and provide shelter, they are often fraught with tension, chaos, and fear.

Why do I keep acting this way? While trauma may take place over days, months or years, the resulting triggers and distorted perceptions can last a lifetime. Here's why. When the limbic system of the brain (part of the mid-brain) reacts to a frightening event, it registers smells, colors, sounds, temperatures, and other sensations associated with the experience. Because the limbic system doesn't know time, anything that is reminiscent of the trauma can result in being a perpetual trigger point. For example, if the sound of footsteps coming toward the door of the house around dinner time followed by a key turning in the lock preceded an angry tyrannical parent entering and screaming or hitting, the limbic system registers all the associated sounds as a signal of impending danger. Thus the physiological alarm system continues to go off years later when one hears footsteps approaching a door or a key turning in a lock. People often judge themselves harshly for not being able to control the physiological responses that are out of their control. They end up saying things such as, "I shouldn't get so upset when I hear footsteps coming or a key in the lock." "I should be over this by now."

It can help to remember that sudden flashes of anger, hurt, rage, shame, or a desire to disappear, are the body reenacting a trauma response that got wired into the system. In other words, the neo cortex--the thinking and reasoning brain--says one thing and our physiology says another. To heal from trauma as well as addiction, it is crucial to address these paired associations at a physiological level with therapies that access the body and the nervous system—EMDR, Body Centered Therapy, Emotional Freedom Technique, and others.

RESPONSES TO TRAUMA AND THE 16 STEPS

This section includes a list of responses to trauma and the corresponding steps that help in the healing/empowerment process. I suggest you have a copy of the 16 steps beside you when you read through the following section so you can match the steps with the trauma responses in a way that makes sense to you. Ultimately, the steps form a hologram of recovery/discovery where all aspects of healing and empowerment relate to each other. You could spin this circle of connections in many directions. For example, clearing out shame and guilt (step 7), helps people speak more honestly with friends and loved ones, which leads to having more authentic supportive relationships (step 3), which in turn lowers anxiety and helps give people the courage to take charge of their life and find the strength to stay clean and sober (step 1). The exercises that accompany each step help deepen the experience of the step. For example, in step 6 people are encouraged to go around the circle and talk about their strengths, creativity, and abilities.

In going through the following, remember that there is no one way people respond to trauma. Everyone makes adaptations based on genetics, environment, temperament and intensity or duration of trauma. The purpose of the following list is to recognize your own patterns and start observing them rather than falling into them. A first step is learning to step back from a situation observe yourself. When you can say, "Wow, I sure flared over that-- I wonder what that was about?" you break the reactive pattern and start gaining control over your reactions. The healing process involves remembering that it is your physiological body and conditioned mind that are being activated. It is not your essential self. At a deeper level you are part of the one universal energy, the flow of all life, sacred because you are alive. The idea is to replace shame and guilt with curiosity and fascination as you learn about yourself. This an important first step toward a more stable, healthy, affirming life.

Thirteen Responses to Trauma and Related Steps
1. Physical, emotional and mental upheaval/disregulation: People have difficulty finding an emotional balance point. They live in extreme states that reflect a fear of being emotionally present. Individuals go from highs to lows, see the world as extremely negative or put on rose-colored glasses. They either are desperate to please *or* feel judgmental and resentful; strive to be the best *or* make little effort to succeed (this may alternate in different situations); have difficulty mobilizing to achieve a task *or* can't stop once started and overwork to the point of collapse. They might idealize others then write them off for disagreeing or not giving unconditional approval. Life is experienced as concrete, linear and two dimensional, and lacks a nuanced understanding of people and situations. **Sixteen step groups provide a safe place for people to express and process feelings. Repeatedly in my interviews, women said that it was the first time in an addiction recovery group where they could safely talk about abuse, pain, loss, discrimination, and fear, and have other people truly listen. When the whole person is invited to be present and feelings are not experienced as dangerous,**

shameful or frightening, people reported that they started to experience a middle ground where they could have feelings but not get lost in them. Another stabilizing aspect of 16-step groups is that participants are encouraged to talk about all aspects of their lives. There are no "outside issues." When the whole person is welcomed and validated, integration of the personality replaces fragmentation. All 16 steps relate to balancing and regulating the emotions because they encourage self care, self knowledge, learning to trust one's inner wisdom, and taking positive action in one's behalf.

2. **Physical imbalance, depletion, and disregulation**. Physical and emotional disregulation go hand in hand. The physical stress of trauma, addiction and chaos leaves the body depleted, exhausted, and unbalanced in a myriad of ways. Hypoglycemia, candida albicans (systemic yeast), food allergies, hormone imbalance, hypothyroid, adrenal fatigue, vitamin deficiencies are a few of the common syndromes that contribute to ongoing depression, anxiety, haziness, inertia, and cravings. **Step 13 is crucial to physical healing along with 2, 3, 5, 7, 12, 16. A huge part of recovery/discovery is to heal the physical body and eat foods that bring clarity and energy to the body and mind. The starting point is to make connections between food, exercise, and sleep with how you feel in terms of mental clarity, energy, vitality and ability to sleep. Good food is medicine and exercise brings oxygen to the cells of the body which, in turn, affects our physical, psychological, and emotional states. When we feel physically well we have greater resilience for handling life's challenges.**

3. **Relationships: fear, uneasiness, chaos and lack of wise trust**. As a result of trauma, people may become either highly mistrustful of others, or naively fail to register red flags related to being seduced, charmed, exploited or misled. Individuals tend to have unequal relationships--are either eager to please and gain approval or take on a tough "I don't need anyone" stance. The fear of one's disowned feelings may result in feeling anxious in the presence of another's emotions or needs. Instead of drawing close when another is in need, the person withdraws leaving their friend/partner alone and hurt. This is often followed by rationalizing and blaming instead of apologizing, because shame prevents them the person from acknowledging the impact of his or her behavior. This results in painful, stressful, injured relationships. This inability to hold another person in one's heart when distraught sets the stage for insensitive, hurtful and sometimes devastating behavior toward a close friend or partner. **Steps 3, 6, 7, 8, 9, 10, 11, 12. These steps refer to being authentic, being open with one's strengths and creativity, letting go of shame, expressing love and gratitude, affirming one's reality, and choosing to be with people who affirm one's self worth and integrity while avoiding people who are hurtful, harmful or demeaning. Step 8 helps people assess their own behavior and start to be aware that their actions and lack of sensitivity impacts others.**

4. **Shame resulting in denial, minimizing, rage or blaming others**--anything to avoid facing the intense feelings of hurt, anger and a sense of being victimized. Shame--a sense of

being inherently defective--is immobilizing or leads people to wear all kinds of masks. It's a dense, heavy, awful feeling. One woman described it as feeling so bad about herself she wished the world will crack open and swallow her up. To mask their shame, people distort or deny the reality of their childhood and how deeply they feel harmed. Some people explode and lash out when someone touches on their shame; others withdraw into a deep dismal hole. **Steps 4, 5, 7, 8, 9. Step 4 helps people reduce shame by putting trauma and abuse in a cultural context. People view their experiences through an exploration of internalized oppression and come to understand how the demeaning voices of the culture-related racism, classism, sexism, and homophobia have infiltrated their minds. This helps people put the "dysfunctions family" concept in a broader context. Steps 5, 7, 8, 9 focus on clearing out shame, taking responsibility for harm one has done to others, and harm that has been done to self as well as expressing love and gratitude, and tapping into awe and wonder.**

5. Difficulty giving and receiving comfort and care from others. Asking for help feels like a weakness and giving to others may feel like giving away a part of oneself. A person may do one or the other, but not create a flow of both. To allow another person to care for us more than we care for ourselves often elicits tears and thoughts of being unworthy. If a person allows love to penetrate their defended heart, it helps create a softening and the beginning of trust. **Steps 3, 5, 6, 7, 12, 16. These steps encourage people to clear out shame and guilt so they feel worthy of giving and receiving care and comfort. These steps encourage people to trust in the healing power of the truth, which means acknowledging that we need and depend on each other, and have the right to choose people who are safe, kind and caring to be around. In addition, Step 9 encourages people to express love and gratitude to others and develop a capacity for awe and wonder.**

6. Low Frustration Tolerance. People give up easily when faced with a challenge, or avoids situations where they are easily triggered, upset, afraid, or not immediately successful. **The focus of the groups is to bond in power and truth. Groups start with the check in—what did you do to take care of yourself this week? This helps participants focus during the week on what they can report to the group. Taking action, self care, and stretching one's limits are given attention and cheers. Step 4 also helps dispel an individual's internal critics and saboteurs that harp away with, "No, you can't," "Who do you think you are?" "Shut up, you're stupid." People are also encouraged to get help for taking on challenging projects, finding resources, and making contacts. (The chapter, "If you feel like a Baby, get a Baby Sitter," from** *Finding Joy* **can be read with this step.) "You don't have to do it alone" could be understood as a secondary theme of** *Yes, You Can.* **See steps 1, 2, 4, 8, 12, 13.**

7. Disconnected from sensations in the body or gets inaccurate signals from the mind. Individuals suffering from trauma and addiction often feel disassociated or disconnected, or can't always rely on body signals for guidance. For some people, the chaotic rise and fall of emotions and body sensations are hard-wired trigger points from the past and not an accurate assessment of current situations. For example, no danger signal goes off when going toward a dangerous or chaotic situation, but fear arises in response to someone expressing kindness and compassion. Thoughts such as, "danger, danger, get away," "they'll hurt you" explode in the mind. These hardwired reactions can result in misinterpreting what others say or do and trigger core beliefs rooted in the past, such as, "You don't care about me. You're abandoning me. You don't love me if you do that," This contributes to chaotic, volatile, unstable ambivalent relationships. **People in groups reported that the support to express feelings and talk about whatever was relevant to their lives was helpful in being able to reconnect with their bodies. Steps 3, 4, 5, 6, 7, 8, 9. See also the exercises that go with these steps. Note: It can be important to have some form of body centered psychotherapy to address these issues because they may need the facilitation of an experienced therapist.**

8. **Difficulty finding one's authentic voice** amidst the internalized voices of parents, abusers, religious teachings, and culture that manifest as saboteurs, censors and critics. The cunning addictive voice often overshadows the will to be clean and sober with permission-giving one liners—"Just this once. You can stop tomorrow. It will feel good; you only live once, and so on. **Step 4 puts addiction and trauma in a cultural context, which helps expand the context to include hierarchy, patriarchy, and the resulting internalized oppression that people absorb and believe it is who they are. Other steps include 1, 3, 6, 10, 11, 12.**

9. **Lack of a clear and nuanced understanding of one's past that helps makes sense of behavior and feelings.** Often the story of the abuse is still seen from child-like eyes with rigid thinking typified by thoughts of good parent/bad parent, good me/bad me, if only I had done something different, it's not fair, and so on. To heal, the story needs to expand to see self and others as multi-dimensional and in a family and cultural context. **Clearing out shame--steps 5 and 7--is key to seeing beyond the self as damaged, unlovable, and helpless. In addition, connecting fully with the reality of the past includes connecting with strong feelings that arise when a person goes beyond denial, minimizing and distorting painful experiences. This requires a supportive group that can lovingly be present to witness another's pain, helplessness, sorrow and rage. Steps: 3, 4, 5, 7, 8, 10, 11, 12, 16.**

10. **Create situations that re-play past trauma in relationships or jobs.** Trauma can leave people with blind spots and a faulty radar system for choosing supportive people or seeing one's part in creating disturbing situations. This can be with friends, partners, children, or in work situations. Breaking old patterns requires treading into unfamiliar territory by owning up to one's destructive behavior, being vulnerable to people who are safe, being willing to leave a destructive situation, and pushing on the limits of one's sense of deservedness. **Step 12**

directly addresses one's right to choose supportive people, along with steps 1, 4, 7, 8, 10, 12 and 16.

11. Impulsive, compulsive, chaotic approach to life. People are drawn to intensity. Chaos and constant change are often used to avoid terrifying memories and the associated feelings. It's like making a lot of noise to dispel the goblins of terror and emptiness. Bills go unpaid, cars are not repaired, medical checkups are avoided, taking time for rest or self-care is rare, or people run up huge debts. A balanced approach to life includes using one's intelligence, intuition, impulse, and memory of the past when making decisions. It includes balancing body, mind, spirit, and needs for self and others.

Why can't I stop doing this? Compulsions are also a form of chaos because they keep a person trapped in trying to lower their anxiety by controlling their external world. Because people feel dissatisfied, jumpy, empty, or uneasy, they shift their focus to external things they can control such as being compulsively tidy, organized, controlling children, having things a certain way or analyzing others. (Note: compulsive means that you can't relax unless the subject of the compulsion is satisfied--it's fine to be tidy, but it becomes problematic when tidiness precludes life affirming activities and relationships with children and loved ones.) Some people live in chaos in some aspects of their life and are compulsive in others. For example, a person might put all kinds of harmful substances in their bodies, yet have an immaculate living space. **Steps 3, 5, 7, 8, 11, 13, 15.**

12. Difficulty with boundaries. Boundaries are like a fence around us--a protective shield to keep us safe. Healing from trauma and addiction involves creating a safety zone for ourselves by determining who is safe to have close, and who needs to be kept at a distance. We also need to become aware of the ways we intrude on others. We can ask ourselves, am I noticing non-verbal cues? Am I getting lost in my own self absorption and failing to notice the reactions and needs of others? Trauma inherently involves boundary violations where someone with more power intrudes, harms, exploits and manipulates another person, usually one with less power. It leaves a person with a faulty internal radar system for assessing their rightful boundaries, meaning the ability to say No, Yes, Maybe, I want to, I don't want to, That's not helpful for me." Unfortunately, fear often arises when we imagine setting these limits--it can feel like breaking a rule or committing a crime. Some people set tight and rigid boundaries--they say no to anything that feels new or risky--while others may exhaust themselves by accommodating others to the exclusion of their own needs. Some alternate between the two extremes. Both reactions are driven by fear and a lack of internal attunement that asks, "What feels right and life affirming in this situation?" Boundary problems often involve role reversals (expecting our children to make us happy), dual relationships (such as being close friends with one's therapist) or triangles (getting involved with a best friends partner). All of these situations run the risk of emotional upset, lost relationships, and harm to others. Boundaries are also internal and an important aspect of defining sobriety: I don't get to go to that bar, see those people, listen to that music, skip work, or isolate. I don't get to say whatever comes to mind--I need to think of how I impact others. I need to connect with others, get rest, sleep, exercise, focus on my strengths and take action to improve my life. Learning to set appropriate boundaries helps us feel safe to say yes to life because we become able to process new information, make informed decisions based on current time, and make changes whenever necessary. **Steps 1, 3, 4, 8, 9, 10, 11, 12, 13,**

13. Lack of sober pleasure, joy and meaning in life. Because people manage trauma with numbing, hyper activity, addictions, and constant running from their internal goblins, the journey toward healing is one of slowing down into stillness so we can feel the beating of our heart and the rhythm of our breathing. We need to face and process whatever emotions and memories arise from the stillness. It can feel like going through withdrawal to slow down the action and drop beneath our restlessness so we can take a walk and notice a blade of grass, feel delight by the sounds of birds, and notice the shapes of clouds. We need to quiet ourselves and deepen our breathing so we can resonate into the heart of things, attune to what others are saying, and feel the rhythms and sensations of our bodies. It's like going through adrenaline withdrawal so we can begin to feel an internal ease and quiet that allows us to experience awe and wonder at simple things. We find that meaning comes from each moment of our experience--being present to it, savoring it, and letting it go. From this quiet place we start to hear our inward guidance about work, relationships, and how to take care of ourselves. **Steps: 1, 9, 13, 15, 16. Step 1 is crucial for intervening on addiction. First, by asserting our power to take charge of our lives, and second, to do the exercise of linking harmful consequences with the addiction. All seven of the exercises are extremely effective in helping people slow down the pace and start their inward journey. Step 9--expressing love and gratitude and feeling awe and wonder--takes us to a high vibration of energy that is healing to every muscle, cell and drop of blood in our body. Shifting our focus to gratitude takes us to new ways of perceiving and experiencing our lives.**
*****

From the author: Bright blessings and all best wishes to you on your special journey. I hope these words help you make sense of your life and lead toward healing. Others have healed from trauma and addiction, you can too. Peace and joy to you. Your sister and friend,

REFERENCES
Kasl C. 1985. Dear Therapist. *Survivors of Abuse Talk with Therapists.*
Kasl, C. 1989. *Women, Sex, and Addiction: A Search for Love and Power*. New York: HarperCollins
Kasl C. 1992 *Many Roads, One Journey, Moving Beyond the 12 Steps*. HarperCollins
Van der Kolk, B.A. & Saporata. J. 1991. The biological response to psychic trauma: Mechanisms and treatment of intrusion and numbing. Anxiety Research, 4, 199-212.

APPENDIX

Hierarchy - Patriarchy

Concept: Charlotte Kasl
Illustration: Lenore Davis
© 1991
Many Roads, One Journey:
Moving Beyond the 12 Steps

Questions for Step Four

Hierarchy, Patriarchy And Our Lives/Addictions

© Charlotte Kasl 1993

Your personal journey on hierarchy *Referring to the hierarchy/patriarchy illustration, have a group discussion on the following questions:*

1. Where were you born on hierarchy? How did it effect your basic belief system? Your sense of personal power? The ability to take care of yourself?

2. a) How have you moved up and down? (through work? relationships? education? marriage? divorce? leaving a high status job? etc?) Where are you now?

   b) How has your journey up and down been affected by *things you did for yourself?*

   c) How has it been affected by the people you associated with, inherited wealth, etc?

   d) Referring to events and experiences from a, b and c:
      — Which of them affirm your humanness, strengths and talents?
      — Which of them led you to deny your humanness, strengths and talents?
      — Which of them created confusion in your life?

3. How has your position in hierarchy and your journey been affected by things you couldn't control—gender, race, sexual preference, age, money, class, cultural background, where you grew up, etc?

4. When were you the happiest? most fulfilled?

5. When were you the least happy? the least fulfilled?

6. When was there the most stress? Talk about the different kinds of stress— from hard work or not having enough to eat or feeling hopeless.

7. When was there the least stress?

8. What elements of this system contribute to addiction?

9. What elements of this system contribute to dependent, violent, painful relationships?

10. What in this system has been good for you?

11. Imagine a social system or society where everyone is appreciated and cared for equally, no matter what.

12. Other questions???

Questions on Hierarchy / Patriarchy

How the system works?

1. Which group of people in this system defined you—your values, strengths, worth?
   - -What did they affirm about you?
   - -What did they teach you that was not in your best interest?

2. Which group of people in this system defined your sexuality?
   - -What definition of sexuality did you learn for yourself?
   - -How has this worked for you?
   - -How has this not worked for you?
   - -How has it been confusing?

3. How does fear operate in this system?
   - -For the ones on top?
   - -For the ones in the middle?
   - -For the ones at the bottom?
   - -What role has fear played in your life?

4. How does the positioning of people in this system affect their ability to feel compassion, empathy, love and care? How has it affected you personally?

5. How do people at every level of this system assert their power and autonomy? Openly? Passively? Cleverly? Tell about ways you have asserted your power?

6. How does this system lead to feelings of guilt and shame? (Through abuse and neglect, racism and sexism?) Do you feel guilt or shame: for wanting to assert yourself? To be tender? To be powerful? To affirm your cultural heritage? To express anger? To express love? To express fear?

7. Think of the general attributes people develop at different levels in the system?
   - -Sense of humor
   - -Intimate, authentic bonding
   - -Joy
   - -Passion, spontaneity
   - -Cleverness
   - -Security (inner and outer)
   - -Fear
   - -Compassion
   - -Understanding and consciousness of the system's impact on different groups of people

8. Tell of particular events in your life that have been deeply affected by this system? Education? Birthing? Developing your talents? Having a full range of emotions? Say what has been positive and what has been negative?

Transformation Exercise

I UNDERSTAND

1. List personal traits that feel troublesome or out of control. You can also include past behavior you haven't forgiven yourself for. It could be for being dishonest to someone, not standing up for yourself, losing your temper, being hard on yourself, or any addictive behavior.

2. Pick out one that has energy for you today, one that you want to change or let go of. Take some time to tune into your breathing and get into a relaxed state. Say to yourself several times: *I am willing to let go of this. I am willing to release this.*

3. With your eyes closed, imagine yourself doing the behavior that troubles you. Summon your compassion and love—your wisest self—and witness yourself doing the unwanted behavior. (If no image comes, just think about it.) Start saying to yourself, *I Understand. I Understand why I did that,* or *I understand why I do that,* or *I understand why you did that.*

4. As you continue to say, *I understand. I understand why you/I do that,* look into your own heart and find the positive intention underneath the behavior.

   Examples:
   I Understand why you drank so much as an adolescent. It's the way you buried your pain about being abused.

   I Understand why you get so quiet. It was how you avoided being shamed.

   I Understand why you are always being good, You're afraid your mother/father will fall apart.

   I Understand why you shoplifted—you were trying to give yourself something special after you father left.

   I Understand why you ate so much, you were trying to fill up the loneliness.
   REPEAT THE REASONS YOU UNDERSTAND UNTIL YOU START TO FEEL A SENSE OF COMPASSION FOR YOURSELF. (If this doesn't happen, try again on a different day.)

5. Now say to yourself with all your heart and love, *"I will never put you down for this again."*

6. Then elicit your wise, adult self and say, *"I understand why you did that, but now we are going to learn better ways to get what we need. Here's what we can do differently.*

7. Think of all the ways you can get what you are yearning for without harming yourself or other people. Go over the possibilities in your mind. Imagine doing them.

8. Take a few moments to come out of the trance state, then write down all the things you can do differently to fulfill you positive intentions without harming yourself or other. Talk about your experience with other group members.

9. Take action! Do them!

Discovery Mandala

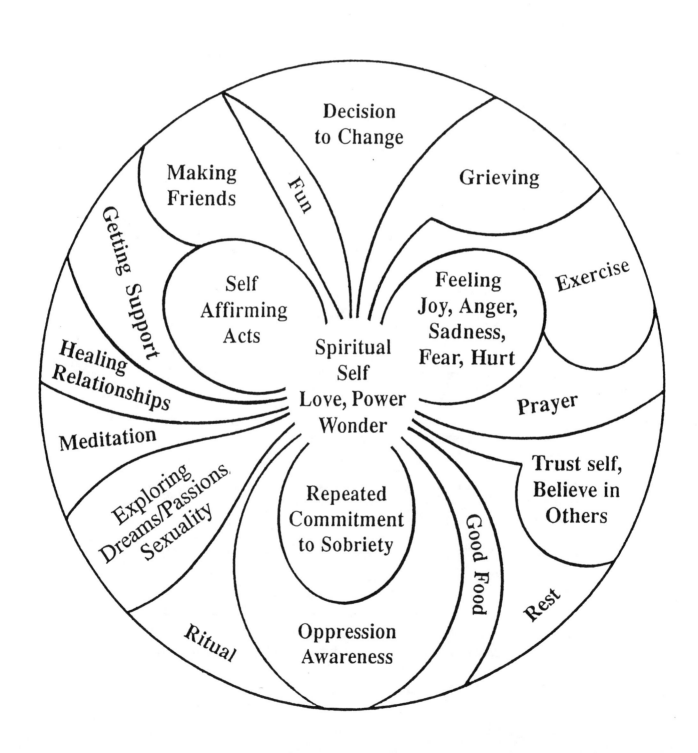

Decision to Change

Making Friends

Fun

Grieving

Getting Support

Self Affirming Acts

Feeling Joy, Anger, Sadness, Fear, Hurt

Exercise

Healing Relationships

Spiritual Self Love, Power Wonder

Prayer

Meditation

Trust self, Believe in Others

Exploring Dreams/Passions Sexuality

Repeated Commitment to Sobriety

Good Food

Ritual

Oppression Awareness

Rest

❖ ○ ✪ ○ ❖

Discovery Mandala

(To fill in)

Directions: Fill in the sections with aspects of your growth.
Indicate how much progress you have made in various areas.

Steps for Recovery and Empowerment for Survivors of Ritual and Other Profound Abuse

Montana Women's Group

1. We recognize that we are powerless over having been profoundly and ritually abused, and that as a result, aspects of our lives have become unmanageable. We recognize that today, we DO have the power to take charge of our healing and living.

2. We have come to believe that there is a Great Spirit/Universe/God/(—) whose presence awakens the healing wisdom within us when we open ourselves to it.

3. We've become willing to hear the Great Spirit speak its truths into our spirits, to receive its great care for us, to listen, and to act based upon these truths and this love.

4. We examine our beliefs, addictions, attitudes and behaviors in the context of having lived in an upside-down culture, and we acknowledge that we presently live within a hierarchal, patriarchal society. We do this thoroughly, with assistance from another or others within this program.

5. We share with another and with the Great Spirit the specific ways we have harmed ourselves and others, discerning the exact nature of the circumstances within which the events occurred, as best we can.

6. We *affirm* and enjoy our strengths, talents, accomplishments, and intelligence, remembering not to hide these qualities in attempts to protect others egos or out of our fear.

7. We strive to become willing to let go of and to work through shame, guilt, negative attitudes and behaviors which prevent us from living full and self-nurturing lives, and which impede our loving ourselves and others.

8. To the best of our ability, we've made a list of all whom we've harmed and have become willing to make amends to each. We've also made a list of key people who have harmed us. When ready, and when it is safe and appropriate, we have taken steps to resolve our issues with them, in abstentia if need be, so that our resentments and fears no longer have power over us.

9. We've made a list of all who have been kind or loving to us, and we've taken steps to thank them.

10. We continue to trust our reality and to daily affirm that we see what we see, know what we know, and feel what we feel. When we know Truth, we promptly admit it as ours, refusing to silence or back away from it.

11. We continue to notice our destructive beliefs, attitudes and behaviors when they occur, making amends where appropriate. But we do not take responsibility or apologize for things we have not done. We refrain from analyzing or covering up the shortcoming of others.

12. We seek out situations, people, and activities that affirm our worth, intelligence, and wholeness, and we avoid situations, people and activities that are hurtful, harmful, or demeaning to us or others.

13. We take steps to nurture and heal our physical bodies, honor our natural emotional healing process, respect our life-seeking and to have fun.

14. We actively work to develop an ever more honest and deepening relationship with that which we call sacred (Great Spirit/Universe/ God), opening to find our inner calling and developing the will and the wisdom to heed and to follow it.

15. We grow in awareness that we are sacred persons, interrelated with all living beings. When ready, in a way that is right for us, we take an active part in helping the planet become a better place for all life.

16. We accept the daily challenges of life as opportunities for our growth, realizing that no event is entirely complete without our response to it.

Principles of Personal Progress

1. Realize that I am not sick but that I am carrying the symptoms of the sick system that oppresses me.

2. Make a commitment to leave the sick system emotionally and put my fully empowered True Self back in charge of my life.

3. Begin to develop a Higher Perspective by learning about the cunning ways of oppressive systems and the promises of personal empowerment.

4. Be angry about being cheated, sad about my losses... and then excited about the possibilities.

5. Demythifize the sick system by telling its secrets rather than acting them out, and practicing personal honesty and boundaries in all the phases of my life.

6. Make it safe for my True Self to emerge by surrounding myself with affirming and nurturing people, including myself.

7. Put my True Self in charge of my life by honoring my needs, realities, and feelings.

8. From my Higher Perspective be open to the spiritual lessons of everyday life.

9. Reparent myself by considering new healthy patterns of behavior and thinking.

10. Take the risks of trying these new behaviors and asking for help if I can not do them alone.

11. Repeatedly practice the behaviors I find effective until they become habit.

12. Celebrate and share with others my new found progress and joy.

Adam W.

Violence Anonymous

1. I am a vital link with all other living creatures. Therefore, my efforts to avoid violence make a difference in bringing peace to the planet. *Peace starts with me.*

2. I am ready to do whatever brings strength and honor to me, my family & community, by stopping negative and violent behavior with the help of a Higher Power and others

3. If I slip backwards into violent behavior patterns I will seek help and begin again.

4. I look inside myself and work to build the personal power I have tried to find through the negative use of guns or violence.

5. I seek solutions to the problems of daily life without the use of violence.

6. I search within to find my strengths and weaknesses, and determine if these attributes have contributed to my victimization of others.

7. I accept personal responsibility for my violent actions and their impact on others.

8. I do not blame others for my circumstances in life, or use them as an excuse for negative and violent behavior.

9. I share with another person inner feelings and thoughts that create guilt and shame.

10. I process any past abuse issues I have experienced in a healthy way without inflicting abuse or violence on others.

11. I seek friends and a sense of belonging without the negative use of control, weapons or violence

12. I do not instigate violence to relieve boredom. I will substitute positive social activities instead of repeating negative behavior.

13. I do not vent anger, revenge or seek thrills with the negative use of firearms or violence and am ready to discard all behaviors no longer healthy for myself and others.

14. I associate with people who encourage me to grow in a positive direction and I avoid situations or people who try to re-engage me in behaviors I want to stop.

15. If my family / neighborhood / school is unsafe, I make a commitment to be part of the solution, not part of the problem.

Copyright 1993
Nancy A. Mapley
Healing Fires Press, Ltd.

NOTE: I have reworded these steps to make them present tense instead of future tense as originally written.

DAILY YIN-YANG EATING WORKSHEET

What I eat/drink	Degree of Yin-Yang	How I feel physically/emotionally	Hours of sleep	Quality of sleep

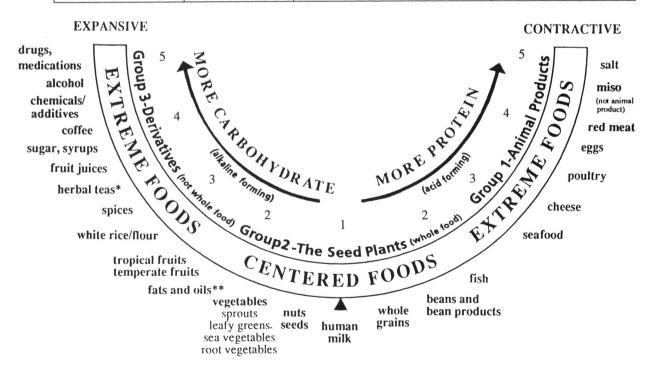

*In general herbal teas vary from yin to yang according to whether they are flower, leaf, seed, or root in that order.

**The effect of oils varies based on whether they are plant or animal derivatives, quality, and method of processing.

Overall, the effect of yin and yang varies based on quality, freshness of food, preparation, cooking time, seasoning, etc.

Adapted from a model by Sol Miller with Jo Anne Miller.   Placement of foods on the scale by Shelley McCoy, certified macrobiotic cook.

SEX ROLES, SEXUALITY AND ADDICTIONS

What have I been taught about my identity/role as a woman/man?

How has my true potential as a human being been *denied* by these teachings?

What dysfunctional/dependent/ addictive behavior is this linked to?

Closings for Meetings

Here are some prayers or meditations that people sent me from existing 16-step groups. Many groups rotate on a weekly basis having someone bring a closing of their choice. You are welcome to use these or find some of your own.
(Many of these were compiled by Indigo Vegan of Dallas, Texas)

An Indian Prayer

O' GREAT SPIRIT,
Whose voice I hear in the winds,
And whose breath gives life to all the world, hear me! I am small and weak, I need your strength and wisdom.

LET ME WALK IN BEAUTY, and make my eyes ever behold the red and purple sunset.

MAKE MY HANDS respect the things you have made and my ears sharp to hear your voice.

MAKE ME WISE so that I may understand the things you have taught my people.

LET ME LEARN the lessons you have hidden in every leaf and rock.

I SEEK STRENGTH, not to be greater than my brother, but to fight my greatest enemy—myself.

MAKE ME ALWAYS READY to come to you with clean hands and straight eyes.

SO WHEN LIFE FADES, as the fading sunset, my spirit may come to you without shame.

The Indian Prayer (above) is a gift from the Sioux Indian children of RED CLOUD INDIAN SCHOOL, Pine Ridge, South Dakota.

Originality exists in every individual because each of us differs from the others. We are all primary numbers divisible only by ourselves.
– Jean Guitton

I want to beg you as much as I can... to be patient towards all that is unsolved in your heart and to try to love the questions themselves.... Do not seek answers which cannot be given you because you would not be able to live them. And the point is to live everything. Live the questions now. Perhaps you will then gradually, without noticing it, live along some distant day into the answer... take whatever comes with great trust, and if only it comes out of your own will, out of some need of your innermost being, take it upon yourself and hate nothing.
Rilke

I don't believe there is a God up there deciding that someone will have a car accident, someone will get cancer, or someone will win the lottery. While there may be a mystical quality to why things happen when they do, and I believe there is a synchronicity that comes when one is following one's path, I believe there is also randomness and unpredictability in life. I believe we have free will, and that God, Goddess, and the Great Spirit are within us all and their work on earth comes through our own efforts. I believe life is sometimes tough, sometimes sweet, and it's how we deal with it that reflects our spirituality and our inner strength.
– Charlotte Davis Kasl,
Many Roads, One Journey

Habondia, the real abundance, is the power to say yes and to say no, to open and to close, to take or to leave, and not to be taken by force or law or fear or poverty or hunger.
– Marge Piercy,
The Sabbath of Mutual Respect

Anything in your life that suffocates you is junk. Anything that crowds the life out of you is junk. That which restricts our living, loving, thinking, and feeling is junk, be it a thing, habit, person, place, or position. Anything that builds, edifies, enriches our spirit—that makes us truly happy, regardless of how worthless it may be in cash terms—ain't junk.

> – Don Aslett,
> *Not For Packrats Only*

Nothing important was ever accomplished without courage and risk.

> – Sonia Johnson,
> *Going Out of Our Minds*

It is not discipline, will power, or pressure from others that facilitates adherence to a challenging course of action; but rather the freedom to choose among alternatives, the personal commitment to a mission, and the willingness to take responsibility for the consequences of one's decisions that steel the will and embolden the spirit.

> – Neil A. Fiore,
> *The Road Back to Health*

Moving toward a live-loving/creative spirituality involves bridging differences by increasing our capacity to accept, understand, and be empathic to different people, their cultures, traditions, and values, and to stop thinking that anyone has a corner on truth or anyone has the right to exploit others. Like the earth, people are not objects to be exploited; rather, we are all part of an interrelated whole. When we think we are right or we exploit others, we become alienated and miss the richness of human love.

> – Charlotte Davis Kasl,
> *Many Roads, One Journey*

Obviously we will never create the new society by crawling into the box of our previous conditioning. We will never find sufficient freedom to realize our full human potential within the confines of the automatic response.... To the extent that we manage to extricate ourselves for the restrictions of previous conditioning, we can start walking freely and purposefully in the wide world of autonomy and self-determination.

> – Ingrid Komar, *Living the Dream: Twin Oaks Community*

Humans have a higher nature which includes the need for meaningful work, for responsibility, for creativeness, for being fair and just, for doing what is worthwhile and for preferring to do it well.

> – Abraham H. Maslow,
> *Eupsychian Management*

Love's Prayer
Blessed Be
Our Mother and Father
The spirit of Love
Who art in heaven and earth,
The seas and the mountains
Our hearts and our bodies.
Hallowed by thy names
And the names of all thy creatures
Thy realm become, thy ever-
	changing will unfold
On earth which is the body of heaven
Give us this day our daily bread
And fill our hunger with love
Help us forgive ourselves
That we may pardon others
And bring all people together in a
	sacred circle
Of mercy, compassion and love.

> – Revised from the
> Feminist Lord's Prayer
> by Charlotte Kasl

BIBLIOGRAPHY

Rather than a huge list of books from the addiction field, (which is available in Many Roads, One Journey), I am including books I have found particularly helpful or interesting relevant to the 16-step empowerment model.

Aslett, Don A. Clutter's Last Stand. Cincinnatti, Ohio: Writer's Digest Books, 1984.

Burns, David D., M.D. Feeling Good: The New Mood Therapy. New York: William Morrow, 1980.

Capra, Fritijof. The Turning Point: Science, Society, and the Rising Culture. New York: Simon & Shuster, 1982.

Christopher, James. How to Stay Sober: Recovery Without Religion. Buffalo, N.Y. Prometheus Books, 1988.

Colbin, Annemarie. Food and Healing. New York: Ballantine Books, 1986.

Common Boundary May/June 1990. "Why Spiritual Groups Go Awry." Edited by Joanne Sanders.

Crook, Whilliam G, M.D. The Yeast Connection: A Medical Breakthough, 3rd Ed. Jackson, Tenn.:Professional Books, 1986

Fowler, James W. Stages of Faith. San Francisco: Harper & Row, 1981.

Fulani, Lenora, Ph.D. The Psychophathology of Everyday Racism and Sexism. New York and London: Harrington Park Press, 1987.

Havel, Vaclav. Lving in Truth. Harlow, Essex: Faber & Faber, 1987.

Kasl, Charlotte Davis. Women, Sex, and Addiction: A Search for Love and Power. New York: Ticknor & Fields, 1989.

_____"Dear Therapist: Through the Voices of Survivors." Self Published booklet, March 1986.Available for $4.00 includes mailing: Box 1302Lolo MT 59847

_____Finding Joy: 101 Ways to Free Your Spirit and Dance with Life. New York: HarperCollins, 1994.

_____Many Roads, One Journey: Moving Beyond the 12 Steps. New York: HarperCollins, 1992.

Larson, Joan Matthews Seven Weeks to Sobriety. The Proven Program to Fight Alcoholism Through Nutrition. New York: Fawcett Columbine 1992.

Magid, Dr. Ken, and Carole A. McKelvey. High Risk.Children Without a Conscience. New York: Bantam Books, 1987.

Miller, Jean Baker, M.D. Toward a New Psychology of Women. Boston: Beacon Press, 1976.

Morgan, Marlow. Mutant Message Down Under. New York: HarperCollins, 1994.

Quinn, Daniel, Ishmael. New York: Bantam/Turner, 1992.

Stokes, Kenneth. Faith Is a Verb: The Dynamics of Adult Faith Development. Mystic, Conn.:Twenty-Third Publications, 1989.

Trimpy, Jack LCSW. Rational Recovery from Alcoholism: The Small Book.California: Lotus Press, 1989.

Wolf, Naomi. The Beauty Myth. New York: William Morrow & Co., 1991.

16 Steps for Discovery and Empowerment

Through the Voices of Many Women and Men

1) We affirm we have the power to take charge of our lives and stop being dependent on substances or other people for our self-esteem and security.

   Alternative: We admit/acknowledge we are out of control with/powerless over _____ yet have the power to take charge of our lives and stop being dependent on substances or other people for our self-esteem and security.

2) We come to believe that God/Goddess/Universe/Great Spirit/Higher Power awakens the healing wisdom within us when we open ourselves to that power.

3) We make a decision to become our authentic selves and trust in the healing power of the truth.

4) We examine our beliefs, addictions, and dependent behavior in the context of living in a hierarchical, patriarchal culture.

5) We share with another person and the Universe all those things inside of us for which we feel shame and guilt.

6) We affirm and enjoy our intelligence, strengths and creativity, remembering not to hide these qualities from ourselves and others.

7) We become willing to let go of shame, guilt and any behavior that keeps us from loving ourselves and others.

8) We make a list of people we have harmed and people who have harmed us, and take steps to clear out negative energy by making amends and sharing our grievances in a respectful way.

9) We express love and gratitude to others and increasingly appreciate the wonder of life and the blessings we do have.

10) We learn to trust our reality and daily affirm that we see what we see, we know what we know and we feel what we feel.

11) We promptly admit to mistakes and make amends when appropriate, but we do not say we are sorry for things we have not done, and we do not cover up, analyze or take responsibility for the shortcomings of others.

12) We seek out situations, jobs, and people that affirm our intelligence, perceptions and self-worth and avoid situations or people who are hurtful harmful, or demeaning to us.

13) We take steps to heal our physical bodies, organize our lives, reduce stress and have fun.

14) We seek to find our inward calling, and develop the will and wisdom to follow it.

15) We accept the ups and downs of life as natural events that can be used as lessons for our growth.

16) We grow in awareness that we are sacred beings, interrelated with all living things, and we contribute to restoring peace and balance on the planet.